THREE CENTURIES
TO CONCORDE

Supersonic flight – the old and the new. The British Aircraft Corporation Type 221, WG.774 (nearest camera), in formation with the second Fairey Delta 2, WG.777. WG.774 was originally built as the first Delta 2 and was identical to WG.777, having the same simple shape of delta wing. In this form it captured the World Air Speed record in March 1956 by achieving 1132 miles/h. Later, WG.774 was lengthened and equipped with the modified delta (ogee) wing shown here. With this wing it was used to investigate flight with separated airflow, a new concept on which the Concorde design was based.

(British Aerospace)

THREE CENTURIES
TO CONCORDE

by

CHARLES BURNET

MECHANICAL ENGINEERING
PUBLICATIONS LIMITED
LONDON

ISBN 0 85298 412 X

Phototypeset by Galleon Photosetting, Ipswich
Printed and bound in Great Britain by
The Garden City Press Limited
Letchworth, Hertfordshire

CONTENTS

FOREWORD
by
The Rt Hon. Julian Amery, MP
(Minister of Aviation, 1962–64)

The present age is bedevilled by an absence of historical perspective and an ignorance of what is going on around us. As to perspective, journalists, politicians, and even trained administrators tend to discuss each new issue as if, like the mule, it had no pride of ancestry or hope of posterity. There seems to be a built-in resistance to seeing where things have sprung from and where they will lead. And yet, as Napoleon wrote, 'Above all, let my son read history. It is the only true philosophy.'

As to ignorance, Arthur Koestler once wrote that every technical progress involves a cultural regress. Our civilization indeed has suffered from the failure of our culture to keep up with the technological revolution through which we are passing. In consequence new developments in science, engineering, and medicine tend to be discussed either in terms so crude and over-simplified as to be meaningless or in specialist jargon comprehensible only to experts.

Mr Charles Burnet has tried, and with considerable success, to correct these two defects where they have bedevilled the discussion of aerospace problems. He has sought to trace a part of British aviation history from the eighteenth century to the Concorde, showing how one development has grown out of another down the years. He has also set out the technical problems involved in terms which the layman can understand.

His book is a purely objective study. It avoids entering into the political and economic merits of the decision to develop Concorde and examines that project simply as a stage in the evolution of a technology which had run out of steam.

Before Concorde we had had considerable experience of supersonic flight by military aircraft. But military aircraft are not designed to fly for long. Training flights are unlikely to total more than a couple of hundred hours a year. Operational flights far less. A supersonic transport on the other hand has to be designed to fly almost continuously if it is to be an economic proposition. To develop Concorde was thus to break wholly new ground and involved solving problems at and indeed beyond the frontiers of knowledge.

Concorde has proved a great technological success. Its value as an individual project has yet to be finally assessed. Mr Burnet makes no attempt to pass a judgement but his book leaves little doubt about the value of the lessons learned. I am confident myself that these and the lead-time secured over their competitors can keep the British and French aerospace industries in the forefront of progress towards the much higher speeds foreseen by Dr Barnes Wallis and others.

Julian Amery

112 Eaton Square, SW1
14 July 1978

PREFACE

In 1943 the science of aeronautics stood on the threshold of a fascinating new era. Forty years had gone by since the American, Orville Wright, had made the first successful flight of a controllable, powered aeroplane, and in that time aircraft speed had risen from little more than a running pace to something around 500 miles an hour.

After centuries of surface travel such progress of course appeared to be massive but it had depended to a large extent on the development of lightweight piston engines and after only forty short years of growth these engines were known to be approaching the limit of their power. For some time therefore a replacement for the piston engine had been sought and had finally been found in the abundant power and simplicity of jet propulsion, but, just when a breakthrough in aeroplane performance seemed likely to follow, the pilots of early jet aeroplanes and indeed of the more advanced piston-engined types began to report the presence of vibrations and loss of control on approaching the speed of sound (760 miles an hour at sea-level).

It had in fact been known for some time that a projectile or any object moving with sufficient speed could compress the air it displaced and that this compression would cause a large rise in air resistance, but as far as the aeroplane was concerned this in itself carried no element of danger and could, given time, be overcome by the jet-propulsion engine. Loss of control on the other hand was an entirely different matter and existing pilot training was of little help in coping with what turned out to be unprecedented situations. It was therefore not long before human life was being lost and when journalists looked for a dramatic explanation for such disturbing events they found it in the phrase 'sound barrier'.

At first used by laboratory workers merely to indicate that air resistance could be a barrier to greater speed it soon came to encompass everything to do with an immense effort needed to fly safely at, and above, the speed of sound. Britain made a significant contribution to this work which culminated in the decision to design and build the Anglo–French supersonic airliner, Concorde, and in this book we follow the path by which British research into the understanding and practice of supersonic flight progressed from early individual experiments, through a period of co-ordinated ground and flight testing, to being first of military and, finally, of commercial use.

The story begins in the first half of the eighteenth century when, as a result of gunnery development, the first known measurements to be made of the air resistance to missiles travelling at very high speeds yielded unexpected results.

ACKNOWLEDGEMENTS

The author would like to acknowledge the assistance of many people who have helped in the preparation of this book.

In respect of particular sections: Foreword, The Right Honourable Julian Amery, MP; Chapter 1, Air Vice-Marshal D. P. Hall, Wing Commander J. Watts-Phillips, The Royal Society for permission to quote from the *Journal Book* of 1671; The National Physical Laboratory; Chapter 2, Air Commodore A. H. Wheeler, Professor W. A. Mair, Mr W. J. Charnley, Mr G. H. Miles, Mr David Lockspeiser; Chapter 3, the late Mr Jack Hanson, Mr L. F. Nicholson, Mr A. E. Gunn, Mr C. Roberts, Wing Commander J. W. Tuson, The Fleet Air Arm Museum, Yeovilton; Chapter 4, Mr R. M. Clarkson, Mr J. Wimpenny, Mr O. Tapper; Chapter 5, Mr D. W. Morgan, Mr P. Amos, Air Commodore P. D. Thorne, Mr R. A. Harvey; Chapter 6, Mr R. Lickley, Mr R. B. Stratton, Mr C. Barnes, Mr A. Puttick; Chapter 7, Air Marshal Sir Gilbert Nicholetts; Chapter 8, Lord Kings-Norton, Professor A. D. Baxter; Chapter 9 and Epilogue, the late Sir Morien Morgan, Mr James Taylor, Mr E. C. Maskell, Mr G. H. Lee, Mr G. Laybourne-Smith, Mr E. Niles Kenyon, Mr Joe Byrne, Mr N. W. Boorer, Mr T. V. Small, Mr John Bagley, Mr David Rendel.

In respect of general assistance throughout the book: Mr H. W. Turner, Air Commodore H. A. Merriman, Mr Peter W. Brooks, and Mr Handel Davies for reading the complete manuscript. Mr Kenneth Warren, MP. Mr Colin Wilson for the drawings of the M52 and the Spitfire XI. Mrs Diane Clegge-Smith for the line-drawings. Mr Allan Gettings and Mrs Lilian Hanson for the loan of documents. Mr D. Childerhouse for his valuable advice and assistance with illustrations. The libraries of the Royal Aircraft Establishment and British Aerospace with particular mention of Mr Dennis Goode, Mr Brian Kervell, and Mr Eric B. Morgan for an almost inexhaustible supply of information.

For getting the book 'airborne' with the first draft type Mrs Lorraine Connell and for being 'landed' with the final type Miss Beryl Clavey. 'En route' Mrs B. Wall, Mrs Pat Beniston, and Mrs Penelope Corden.

For permission to publish various quotations, pictures, or diagrams: the Royal Air Force, the Ministry of Defence, British Aerospace, the Royal Aeronautical Society, the Institution of Mechanical Engineers, Flight International, Sheffield Newspapers Limited, Messrs Rolls-Royce Limited, Messrs Publifoto, Messrs Titanium Metal and Alloys, Short Bros. and Harland.

Finally, the author would like to acknowledge the existence of many others, some famous, others not so famous, whose names have not found their way into the text. This is not because their contribution to the work described was in any way lacking in merit but merely because space did not permit.

1

THE AGE OF MOBILITY

To the inhabitants of the British Isles the arrival of the year 1700 was hardly a reason for rejoicing: brutal penalties still existed for the wrong-doer, medical treatment was crude and offered little comfort to the sick, the highwayman sought his chance to rob the unfortunate traveller, and poverty was an all too common state. The quality of human life was not in fact a thing of which the luckiest could boast and a motley collection of manual skills, religions, and philosophies marked the limit of its scope.

In their sparsely populated lands, divided both by distance and by language, the peoples of Earth were yet to acquire the organized learning which today we call progress; they thus remained the pawns of local dogma and tradition, unable to unite in the cause of their own welfare and knowing little of themselves, their planet, or the universe so clearly visible at night.

Then, as this eighteenth Christian century was born, and the struggle for survival in war, in politics, and in trade forced men to seek new powers, their needs began to fertilize the growth of modern science and so prepare the way for better days. In England, a scientific society was founded about the year 1660. It attracted the interest of King Charles II and soon became known as the Royal Society, a title which it holds to this day. Consisting at first of distinguished men, meeting by mutual consent, the Royal Society quickly grew in authority, and on 21 December 1671 one of the most significant events in its history occurred, when 'The Lord Bishop of Sarum proposed for candidate Mr Isaac Newton, professor of the mathematiks at Cambridge'. (*Journal Book of The Royal Society*, 1671.)

Newton was born in 1642 and of his many contributions to science perhaps none were greater than his laws of gravity and motion; laws essential to the design of efficient machines. Yet, when first revealed, these laws were somewhat limited in use; machines were powered as ever by

1

natural forces, by men, by animals, by water, or by wind, and the heating of a fuel to yield great power in compact form was a process still not fully understood. In the world at large there was therefore very little motion and the power of steam, although observed in ancient times, had not as yet become the first, decisive, substitute for nature.

In Newton's later years, however, a Devonshire blacksmith, Thomas Newcomen, in partnership with one Captain Thomas Savery, completed a steam engine capable of working both continuously and with reasonable economy, a combination not displayed by other similar or earlier designs. The Newcomen engine first saw service in 1711 in answer to a need for greater water pumping capacity in mines and towns: it was massive and slow moving and unsuitable for driving other machines, but when that legendary engineer James Watt (1736–1819) was asked to repair a Newcomen engine he saw how to convert it into a lightweight, quick acting, portable system. A means of mechanical propulsion was then available and the way was opened to that unprecedented era of innovation, the Industrial Revolution.

The result was a gigantic economic and social shock nowhere more obvious than in the field of transportation; an age of mobility had dawned and when steam-powered vehicles first clanked their way across both land and sea it must have seemed to many of the simple-minded population that the devil himself had arrived to stay. Wheels which had depended for their gentle turning on the sweat of man and beast were now to be driven relentlessly by this new-found power from fire; sails which had captured the wind for many a ship were to make way for smoking, sooty, funnels; the dream of human flight was at last to become reality and speed was to be adopted as the god of things to come.

So for good or for ill, in peacetime and in war, the people were going to travel as never before, and whether to trade, to fight, or merely to observe they would go with new assurance to the remotest parts of Earth.

Despite some emotional appeal, speed was not the first requirement of this mobile new economy – of far greater importance was the production of sufficient power to move both passengers and freight in bulk and to keep them on the move in a way that neither animal nor human strength had previously allowed. Not until the coming of the aeroplane did speed itself transform the habits of the common man and only then when airborne crossings of the oceans could be made at speeds approaching that of sound.

2

It might therefore be seen by some as a prophecy that even before James Watt had made mechanical transport possible, an English mathematician, Benjamin Robins (1707–51, and later Sir Benjamin), should have measured the speed of objects moving faster than sound, thus anticipating by some two and a half centuries the ultimate destiny of artificial power in conquering the barriers both of sound and space.

Why in fact was Robins performing this work some 250 years ago? Man had after all never flown despite innumerable years of encouragement from the birds, so why had the speed of sound become important at this time? The answer could be found in the science of gunnery and in particular in the calculation of range. The range of a gun depended on the speed of the shot and this in turn depended on the power of the firing charge (just as a football goes farther the harder it is kicked). A bit more power gave a bit more speed and a bit more speed gave a bit more range – at least according to the theory of the day; but as the demands for increased range were met by shots of even greater speed each gain of speed beyond a certain point was seen to give but little in the way of greater range. Something was causing the higher speed shots to fall short of the calculated target points and Robins was trying to find the reason why. Isaac Newton had hinted that air resistance might be a contributory factor but to men who had never travelled faster than the speed of a horse it was difficult to see how anything as thin as air could cause a shot to fall to earth too soon. Robins, however, showed that such indeed was the case and to do this he invented the ballistic pendulum (Fig. 1), a device consisting simply of a large weight attached firmly to the bottom of a freely swinging arm. A shot was fired at the weight, the force of impact swung the weight a certain distance and this distance then became a measure of the impact speed. At low impact speeds the pendulum swung to the predicted distance; at high speeds the swing was much less than expected and Robins deduced quite rightly that, before impact, the speed of his faster shots was reduced by a very large air resistance and that this same air resistance was causing the gunner's shots to fall short.

Now this alone was news enough but Robins made the further discovery that at any speed the air resistance, or drag, of an object depended not only on its speed but also on its shape, and for this result he made the first ever use of a whirling arm to measure aerodynamic loads.

Robins we must suppose never imagined in his wildest dreams that ordinary people would one day fly as fast as the shot from a gun, but his

3

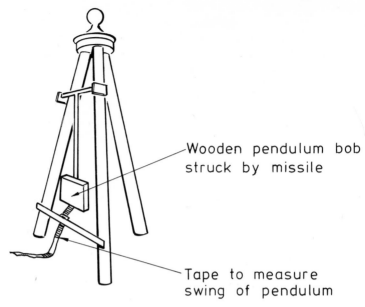

Wooden pendulum bob
struck by missile

Tape to measure
swing of pendulum

*Figure 1. The ballistic pendulum of Sir Benjamin Robins (1707–51) used to
measure speed of missiles travelling faster than sound.*

work was nevertheless the origin of modern aerodynamics. He showed
how subtle and how brutal could be the forces of the air and, in particular,
how the speed of sound could be a barrier to progress.

The rest of this chapter therefore bridges the gap between the days of
Robins and the coming of the supersonic aeroplane; it outlines the
development of flight and the growth of the supersonic problem, and
finally it explains the nature of the sound barrier in simple terms and why
it increased the difficulty of aeroplane design.

We have just learned that the earliest controlled aerodynamic experiments were aimed at measuring drag, and then only on wingless
projectiles. As far as any hope of flight was concerned the primary
requirement was, of course, to produce lift, and this could be done by
moving an object of any shape or size at sufficient speed through the air.
But movement meant drag, drag had to be overcome by power, extra
power meant extra weight, so drag had to be as low as possible. This called

4

for the special properties of a fixed, as opposed to a flapping, wing; a system which Sir George Cayley (1773–1857) was the first to understand when he stipulated that men would fly not by imitating instinctively the flapping wings of birds but by using a fixed surface inclined at an angle to the line of flight and propelled by some means of artificial power. To quote his own words:

The idea of attaching wings to the arms of a man is ridiculous enough, as the pectoral muscles of a bird occupy more than two thirds of its whole muscular strength whereas in man the muscles that could operate upon the wings thus attached would probably not exceed one tenth of the whole mass. There is no proof that weight for weight man is comparatively weaker than a bird; it is therefore probable if he can be made to exert his whole strength advantageously upon a light surface similarly proportioned to his weight as that of the wing of a bird that he would fly like a bird. The flight of a man by great muscular exertion, though a curious and interesting circumstance inasmuch as it will probably be the first means of ascertaining this power and supplying the basis wherein to improve it, would be of little use. I feel perfectly confident, however, that this noble art will soon be brought home to man's general convenience, and that we shall be able to transport ourselves and families, and their goods and chattels, more securely by air than by water, and with a velocity of from 20 to 100 miles an hour. To produce this effect it is only necessary to have a first mover, which will generate more power in a given time, in proportion to its weight, than the animal system of muscles.

This was the first ever definition of the modern aeroplane layout and Cayley demonstrated his ideas with the aid of gliders, one of which is alleged to have carried a thoroughly frightened servant aloft as the first ever occupant of a heavier-than-air free flying device. If only he had had access to a suitable power unit it is acknowledged that Cayley could well have made the first ever powered flight but whether this would have been under full control is another matter. Cayley therefore went as far as it was possible to go at the time in promoting practical aviation, and in 1816 he attempted to form an aeronautical society which did not materialize for another fifty years until the present-day Royal Aeronautical Society was founded.

The next significant step forward in the search for lift is attributed to F. H. Wenham (1824–1908), incidentally a founder member of the Royal Aeronautical Society. Wenham, who had spent some time in Egypt where he had made an intensive study of bird flight, concluded that the majority of wing lift came from the forward portion just aft of the leading edge

5

where the air is accelerated as the wing thickness increases, and his logical conclusion was that an efficient wing should be mostly leading edge – in other words the span should be large compared with the distance between the leading and trailing edges. He was in fact correct, but although adding to the knowledge of what happened, Wenham's work, like that of many others, still did not add much to the understanding of how lift was produced, and it was left to a great experimental engineer, F. W. Lanchester (1868–1946) and a member of the Lanchester motor-car family, to explain precisely how lift was generated and could be calculated using the concept of circulation, in which air, instead of being deflected downwards after passing over a wing surface, was deflected by a rotating 'cylinder' of air.

But the time was approaching when the problem of controlling an aeroplane would have to be faced; how to make it go where required and how to keep it under control when disturbed by atmospheric gusts. Lanchester also laid down the basis for these aspects of flight by investigating systematically the stability characteristics of a remarkable series of flying models.

By the turn of the nineteenth century the conquest of the air was thus very near although it still depended on finding a suitable engine. Once somebody did manage that first vital flight, however, progress would then depend not only on the design of specific aircraft but also on an understanding of the environment in which they flew, and in this respect it is doubtful if any scientist or engineer, British or otherwise, made a more profound contribution to aeronautics than Osborne Reynolds, one-time Professor of Engineering at the University of Manchester. Reynolds was not a member of the aviation fraternity as such but in 1883 he showed that when a fluid (i.e., a liquid or a gas) flowed next to a surface the flow could be either steady or turbulent according to a formula relating the size of the surface to the speed, the density, and the viscosity (or stickiness) of the fluid. (NOTE: Viscosity is a measure of resistance to change of shape and is most important in fluid flow work. It does not depend on density – a good illustration being the liquid metal mercury which has a very high density but is very 'runny', so is said to have a low viscosity.)

Now Reynolds found that the nature of fluid flow was determined not only by how quickly a fluid of a certain density passed over a surface but also on the disturbances within the fluid itself and the latter were determined by viscosity.

The solution to the formula was, conveniently, a simple number later known as Reynolds number, and Reynolds found that in a particular fluid the change from steady to turbulent flow and vice versa always took place at some particular value of the formula. In other words the behaviour of a fluid at any one time was explained by the Reynolds number as a whole and not by any of its elements separately. For instance, a small aeroplane moving at high speed could have the same Reynolds number as a large aeroplane moving at low speed; a common factor that enabled models to be used both in wind-tunnels and in free flight to determine the likely behaviour of a full-sized aircraft.

It was thus possible to predict whether a molecule of air would follow a desired path or not and this was the real secret of flight. If the airflow over a wing followed the shape of the wing then a large quantity of lift could be gained at the expense of a small amount of drag. If on the other hand the flow was to break down into turbulence the lift might be partly or even totally destroyed.

Flying progressed from being merely a dangerous sport to being of widespread practical value only because the flight paths of aeroplanes could be predicted and controlled, and Osborne Reynolds made what turned out to be the greatest single contribution of all to this process.

The achievement of steady flow was therefore a main preoccupation in the early days of aviation, but the possibility of using other flow patterns advantageously had to be considered later when the more demanding requirements of supersonic flight complicated the issue.

Eventually, the inevitable of course happened, and in 1903 the Wright brothers in America made the first controlled flight of a powered aeroplane. This was not a lucky break, nor was it the result of reckless bravery. The Wrights were careful workers; they made their own wind-tunnel; they developed their own engine and they made more than a thousand glider flights, many of them to investigate the mysteries of flying controls. Their success was thus hard earned and deserved.

In the following years a rash of experimental aeroplanes appeared, many of which never flew, many of which had no chance of flying; and the toll of lives was enough to deter the faint-hearted, but the achievements of the pioneers although not always understood were closely followed by the general public, thanks to the appearance of excellent aeronautical journals which contained both news and technical articles. In the British journal *Aeronautics* in 1911, an account appeared of current work on wing design which contained the following comment on the likelihood of flight near the speed of sound:

> Suppose for instance – an extreme case – that the forward speed of the machine could exceed 1,100 feet per second – i.e. the velocity with which air pressure is propagated through the atmosphere . . . there could no longer be any up-current induced in front of the plane (i.e. the wing) and the leading edge would become parallel to the flight path. Although beyond the range of possibility for the aeroplane itself, it is yet quite possible to conceive that the tip speed of propellers might approach this.
>
> Fig. 3 is a shadow picture of a bullet photographed by the electric spark method in 1/12th million of a second on a Schleussner Rapid 'Observatory' Plate. The sharpness of outline is very noticeable. The bullet is moving forward at 1,500 feet per second, and at the same time spinning round on its axis at about 2,000 revolutions per second. The different densities of the disturbed air are clearly reproduced, and also the wake of flocculent and broken matter, which is flowing in to fill up the low pressure region in rear of the base. In front of the nose is a bow-wave of compression, inclined at a sharp angle. The irregularities on the surface of the bullet also gives rise to a minor series of waves. The interesting point to note is that air waves are only formed if the bullet is travelling at a higher rate of speed than the velocity of sound, viz. 1,100 feet per second. In photographs of bullets moving at less than 1,100 feet per second, there is no bow-wave of compression preceding the bullet.

The Fig. 3 mentioned in the quotation is shown in Photograph 1. It is clear from this extract that even the informed opinion of the day foresaw little prospect of flight at anything like the speed of sound, the bullet and shell being the accepted kings of this domain, but the observations are of great interest in the light of the happenings described from now on.

It will be noted that mention is made of air compression being associated with objects moving at the speed of sound and it was this compression that caused the high resistance measured by Robins. The first known British photographs of compression waves, or 'shock' waves as they came to be called, are those of Charles Vernon Boys, FRS (1855–1944), Assistant Professor of Physics at the Royal College of Science from 1889–97.

They were taken in 1892 during a study of bullets in flight and one cannot help reflecting on how fascinated Sir Benjamin Robins might have been to see such visual evidence of his findings. Many years later photography played an indispensable part in the understanding of supersonic flight; without it the formation and movement of shock waves could

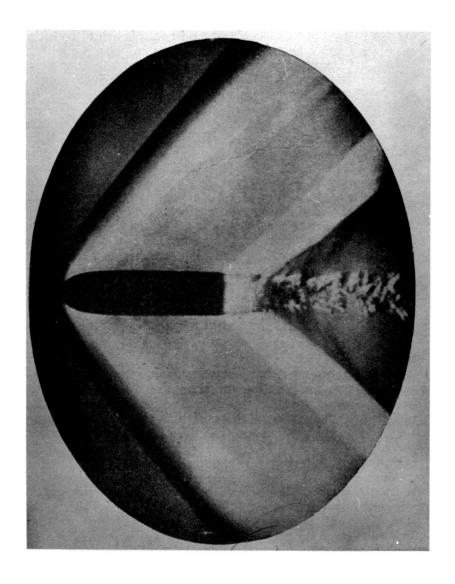

*Photograph 1. Early shadow picture of bullet moving at about 1000 miles/h.
Compression or 'shock' waves can be seen.
(Aeronautics, 1911)*

9

never have been studied and without such study the effects of various aerodynamic shapes would have been difficult to determine with certainty. This is perhaps the place to mention that, in aerodynamic terms, an aeroplane speed is not just faster than sound (supersonic) or slower than sound (subsonic). An 'in between' speed exists known as transonic (roughly 30 per cent below to 30 per cent above the speed of sound), in which the airflow over the surfaces can be a mixture of subsonic and supersonic due to changes in surface curvature. We shall learn of this increasingly as we go along but for the time being let us say that any mixture is usually difficult to get right and the transonic flight mixture was at first unusually difficult.

By 1914, and after eleven years of practical manned flight, aviation remained, however, a mixture of experiment, joy riding, and sport with comparatively small aeroplanes. Some interest had been shown in the potential of aircraft for military purposes, mostly in the reconnaissance role, but the state of the art did not extend to their use for large-scale transportation. Then came World War I and with it came long-range heavy bombers which formed the basis for a first generation of intercontinental passenger and freight air services; the ultimate possibility being well demonstrated in 1919 by the first non-stop transatlantic flight of Alcock and Brown in a Vickers bomber known as the Vimy.

The speeds of all aeroplanes, whether large or small, were nevertheless still low, but after the war finished in 1918, a golden age of speed achievement dawned on a sensation-hungry world. On land, sea, and in the air, one speed record after another tumbled before a sustained onslaught of individual courage and ingenuity the like of which may never be seen again. Outstanding among the successes of this period were the Schneider Trophy air races, this trophy finally being won outright by the British in 1931 when Flight Lieutenant J. N. Boothman (later Air Chief Marshal Sir John N. Boothman), flying a Supermarine S6B seaplane (Photograph 2), returned a speed of 340·08 miles/h. In the same year, Flight Lieutenant G. H. Stainforth (later Wing Cdr, killed in action 1942) flew the S6B, fitted with a specially prepared Rolls-Royce engine, to a world speed record of 407·5 miles/h – or just over half the speed of sound, the first time that 400 miles/h had been exceeded. So what had, in 1911, been considered impossible was, just twenty years later, half-way to becoming reality. In another twenty years it was, of course, an established fact.

Photograph 2. Supermarine S6B Schneider Trophy Seaplane seen here at Calshot. This was the first aircraft to exceed 400 miles/h (29 September 1931). (Supermarine–Vickers Limited)

For Britain, the Schneider Trophy only continued because of the generosity of one Lady Houston. Meanwhile, a strangely mixed-up state of affairs existed behind the scenes. In 1927, and in anticipation of speeds to come, an English mathematician, the late H. Glauert, evolved a simple formula for predicting the lift of a wing under compressible airflow conditions. Glauert's formula was not accurate beyond about 80 per cent of the speed of sound but as a means of initiating design and testing up to this point it proved invaluable. In view of this theoretical work and the very high speeds then being attained in flying contests it might be thought that official policies of the time would have been directed towards the future, but nothing of the sort occurred. A pacifist mood had, not surprisingly, arisen after World War I, and this, coupled with dire economic problems, resulted in a complete lack of interest in the pace-setting development of military aviation; so both military and civil aircraft requirements continued to specify untidy looking biplanes and

11

progress towards the modern monoplane slowed down. As a result, Professor Melville Jones of Cambridge University saw fit to publish, in 1929, a classic paper and lecture emphasizing how the performance of aircraft could be improved by streamlining. By showing the great waste of power resulting from the drag of bracing wires, struts, rivets, and the generally rough surfaces of existing designs he promoted a realization of how stagnant a situation had arisen; so while one part of British aeronautical research was already thinking of transonic flight another part was having to expend much effort in suppressing a primitive design philosophy. To be fair there was indeed some reason for caution. The early history of the monoplane had been strewn with structural failures and fatalities, many of them attributed simply to the weakness of materials, and it is worth noting that even the Supermarine Chief Designer, R. J. Mitchell, was concerned that the racing seaplane work might leave too little time to investigate more general monoplane problems. It should not be overlooked, however, that early aeroplanes had fabric-covered wings and that the fabric contributed nothing to the stiffness of the structure. The braced biplane was a simple way to compensate for what the fabric failed to provide and only when metal skinning was developed did lightweight monoplanes come into their own.

But even metal skins were not a 'cure-all' and it was being realized increasingly that whilst an aircraft structure might not break under a certain load it might nevertheless distort sufficiently to cause significant changes of external shape and that the resulting changes of airflow pattern might cause a loss of stability and control. Severe vibrations of the control surfaces or even of the wings might also be experienced, a phenomenon we now call flutter.

In other words a structure had to be stiff as well as strong; it was allowed to bend, but not too much, and as an example of what might happen there were many cases of flying controls being reversed in their action due to excessive structural distortion. It quickly became clear therefore that designers would need guidance on how stiff to make their structures. In 1932, after considerable theoretical study, two scientists from the Royal Aircraft Establishment (RAE), Farnborough, Hampshire – A. G. Pugsley (later Sir Alfred Pugsley) and Dr H. Roxbee Cox (later Lord Kings Norton) – laid down design requirements, thereby creating the new science of aeroelasticity, a descriptive name attributed to themselves.

Fortunately for the British, however, the Supermarine team which in

1928 had become part of the Vickers organization was not deterred from pursuing the high-speed monoplane and the story of how their racing seaplanes were developed into the legendary Spitfire fighter needs no repetition here. What is less widely known is the part played by some experimental Spitfires in making the first piloted penetrations of the transonic regions for premeditated flight research purposes; a diversion from warlike activities which enabled these elegant aeroplanes to provide advanced information for the design of their jet-propelled successors. This work was performed during a series of high-speed tests in 1943 and 1944 at the RAE Farnborough, and will be examined in the next chapter, but at this stage we must say that a Spitfire achieved a maximum speed of just over 90 per cent of the speed of sound in a dive, a remarkable feat for a piston-engined design of 1936 origin and not to be exceeded for nearly five years by any other British aeroplane, jet propelled or otherwise, and never by a piston-engined machine of any nation.

In later times Supermarines went on to build the Royal Navy's first front-line jet fighter, the Attacker, from which was developed the Swift, the first home-produced fighter aircraft capable of diving faster than sound to enter squadron service with the Royal Air Force, and although the firm no longer functions many of its personnel still work for the now nationalized concern of British Aerospace. So the later versions of the Spitfire and their contemporaries were the last of the great piston-engined fighters and they performed well with the power provided, but the production of power depended on how rapidly a fuel could be burned, and future aeroplanes were going to need an engine capable of burning fuel much more rapidly than hitherto.

The piston engine was in fact a stop–go affair. A mixture of fuel and air had to be sucked repeatedly into each of its cylinders, compressed, burned, and then expelled as exhaust, and although four piston strokes (two down and two up) were needed to complete these actions the power was produced only on the burning stroke when the hot mixture expanded to push the piston down. This system was, however, for many years the only means of obtaining sufficient engine compression to make the fuel consumption of an aeroplane economically acceptable, and although engineers strove to replace the piston engine with a smooth running power turbine driven by continuously compressed and burning gases they were thwarted by the lack of a rotating compressor that really could compress and by turbines of similarly low efficiency.

Then in 1926, the late Dr A. A. Griffith of the RAE (and latterly with Rolls-Royce) applied aerodynamic principles to rotary compressor and turbine blade design; the idea being to guide air carefully over the blade surfaces as with an aeroplane wing, thus avoiding the power losses arising from flow breakdown. British finances did not, however, allow the immediate translation of these ideas into practice although it should be noted that Griffith's initial aim was merely to replace the piston engine – the thrust for forward motion still being supplied by a conventional propeller for reasons of fuel economy.

But a separate, and in some ways simpler, line of research by the then Flight Lieutenant Frank Whittle of the Royal Air Force was destined to become the mainspring of world-wide turbine engine development. Whittle saw the new powerplant not only as a substitute for the piston engine but also for the propeller whose thrust was to be replaced by the hot exhaust gases expelled at enormous speed from the rear of the turbine engine. This system, known as jet propulsion, was capable of increasing aircraft speed far beyond anything expected with the Griffith proposals and although it involved much higher fuel consumption the threat of war made speed the primary target.

Thus it happened that on 15 May 1941, after several years of sometimes heartbreaking work on a severely limited budget, Britain's first turbine powered aircraft, the jet-propelled Gloster–Whittle E28/39, secretly made its maiden flight. The location was the Lincolnshire airfield of Cranwell, home of the Royal Air Force College, and the engine was designed and built in accordance with the pioneer schemes of the man who is now Sir Frank Whittle. Intensive development flying then took place during which an encouraging picture was obtained of jet engine behaviour, and contracts were awarded to Gloster Aircraft Limited for the construction of a twin-engined jet fighter and to the de Havilland Company not only for a single-engined jet fighter but also for a new jet engine. These two aircraft, known as the Gloster Meteor and the de Havilland Vampire, first flew on 5 March 1943, and 20 September 1943, respectively, and the Meteor saw action at the end of the 1939–45 war when called upon to deal with flying bombs. The Germans had in fact been the first to fly a jet-propelled aeroplane in 1939 but their early thinking on gas turbine development was not as comprehensive as Whittle's and for this reason Britain gained a lead in the new technology.

Both the Meteor and Vampire were thus able to give Britain considerable experience of sustained transonic flight as opposed to the short duration dives of the Spitfire, but as neither could exceed the speed of sound, and indeed were slower even than the experimental Spitfires in a dive, they were of limited value for research purposes. What was really needed, of course, was a new style of wind-tunnel capable of much higher speeds – but even this was not, alone, enough. At transonic tunnel speeds the shock wave patterns on a model could be severely affected by waves coming off the tunnel walls. The forces acting on a model might then not represent anything like, either in magnitude or position, the results to be expected in full-size flight, and only in fairly recent years have transonic wind-tunnels become a significant research tool.

In the 1940s it thus seemed clear that research at transonic speeds and beyond, if anybody ever got there, would depend heavily on manned aircraft, albeit on a 'suck it and see' basis. It was known that large surface curvatures would have to be avoided to prevent the breakdown of airflow and to minimize drag but this was about the only certainty. The real problem in fact was that of control in the presence of shock waves, when the smallest of control movements could cause havoc with the airflow over the best of aircraft shapes, or, alternatively, control forces could be so high as to prevent movement by the pilot. To add to the problem, acceptable aerodynamic shapes could create structural complications for which recognized solutions had not been established.

It was therefore considered that special aircraft might be needed to investigate the separate aspects of supersonic flight and that if the speed of sound were to be reached and perhaps exceeded at an early stage some guidance would be available on how best to conduct the future research programmes. As a result the Air Ministry issued the somewhat ambitious specification E24/43 in 1943 for an experimental supersonic aircraft and, in response, the Miles Aircraft Company prepared a design study subsequently known by its type number M52. Construction work actually began on this project but was stopped in February 1946 for reasons which are still the subject of misguided controversy. Photograph 3 is an artist's impression of the M52 as it might have looked had it flown and some idea can be gained of the advanced appearance of this design when compared with its contemporaries. It is hard, having become accustomed to supersonic shapes, to recall the feeling of awe at first aroused by this futuristic looking craft, incorporating as it did major innovations in aerodynamics, engines, flying controls, and aircrew escape equipment.

15

Photograph 3. Artist's impression of Miles M52 supersonic research aircraft as it might have looked had it flown.
(Colin Wilson)

Until then even the most advanced aircraft could be flown by those with a moderate amount of experience but the M52 was going to be different in that no previous experience of supersonic speed existed.

Designed in the new mode to be part of a comprehensive national experiment it came to be regarded as the means by which Britain could have become the first nation ever to achieve supersonic flight. On purely technical grounds there were those who doubted both its capabilities and usefulness but this has been the lot of every attempt at a technical breakthrough and the M52 was no exception. Although abandoned as a full-size machine that was not quite the end of the story, because construction began on a series of twenty-five rocket-propelled scale models of about ¼ size. These were to be dropped off the Scilly Isles from a converted Mosquito bomber and hopes were expressed that some would then fly faster than sound for long enough to obtain worthwhile aerodynamic information. Data was to be transmitted by radio signal to a ground receiver. The first experiment took place on 8 October 1947, but despite considerable effort this project, like its full-size parent the M52, was abandoned in the face of technical problems which made it economically unjustifiable following the world's first manned supersonic flight by the American Bell X-1 on 14 October 1947, and in the light of general progress with other manned designs. One of the models did, however, achieve 930 miles an hour (about 1½ times the speed of sound) and appeared to be under control.

As the new high-speed aircraft could easily be expensive, a Britain impoverished by war therefore had to find some way of cost limitation, and a course of action both technically sound and economically sensible was planned both by Government authorities and private firms, the idea being to use piloted, miniature versions of projected designs – a technique, incidentally, now being considered for future American supersonic airliners. In this way considerable knowledge of the behaviour of different wing and fuselage shapes was assembled to give comparison with wind-tunnel measurements. Straight wings, swept wings, flying wings, delta wings, crescent wings, and numerous forms of engine air intake underwent protracted flight tests. Out of it all came not only a wealth of data and experience but, in the early stages, the first supersonic flight by a British aircraft on 6 September 1948. The history-making machine, built as a private venture by the de Havilland Aircraft Company Limited, was known as the Type 108 and was not in fact part of the national transonic research programme. Conceived to undertake research for later projects and particularly for a proposed jet-propelled airliner, subsequently to become the Comet, the 108 nevertheless became in its own right an object of great significance to British aerodynamic science. Two of the type were originally built, the first to explore low-speed and the second high-speed flight régimes. Both were simply tailless conversions of Vampire fighters, but when the second crashed, tragically killing Geoffrey de Havilland, Jr, son of the firm's founder, a replacement machine of similar shape but greatly modified was built. It was in the third de Havilland 108 that a de Havilland test pilot, the late John Derry, continued to investigate high-speed control until finally this combination of man and machine emerged as Britain's supersonic champion.

This was only eleven months after the American success although there was one significant difference between the two efforts. The American

17

Bell X-1 was a rocket-propelled aircraft, not intended to take off under its own power, but which had to be lifted to high altitude under a B29 bomber and then released. Once its rockets had burned out the return to base and landing required a predetermined descent pattern purely at the mercy of gravity, a technique possible only in a country such as America with vast open spaces away from other air traffic. The de Havilland 108, on the other hand, lacking these facilities, had to be an aeroplane capable of both take off and landing under its own power and of sustained flight, an ability admirably demonstrated in April 1948 when it gained the International 100 km closed circuit speed record at an average of 605·23 miles/h.

It may be thought that the de Havilland 108 success marked the end of a struggle and that it remained only to reap the rewards. This was not the case. Rather was it an early phase in a prolonged battle of attrition which, before it was over, cost the life not only of John Derry but of many of his contemporaries. In the years 1947 to 1953 one prototype after another took to the air, and whilst British knowledge of the sound barrier slowly increased the necessary experiments could only be conducted in diving flight as even the second generation jet engines did not have the power to make this possible in level flight or in a climb. The need for diving, whilst undesirable from safety aspects, did, however, produce the first experience of an interesting byproduct known as the supersonic bang. This phenomenon, caused by shock waves from an aircraft during a dive, sounded like an explosion, which in effect it was, although not of chemical origin. Heard and felt over wide areas each bang stirred the imagination of the general public and, for once, aircraft research became a part of daily life and not something hidden behind walls or tucked away in remote corners of the sky. The whole idea was thrilling even though it meant a few broken windows. Claims for property damaged by the bangs flooded in and found their way into the 'proper channels'. Some were clearly frivolous and others an attempt to have long-tolerated faults rectified free of charge. Eventually enthusiasm waned; the bangs were regarded merely as a nuisance and special high-speed flying areas with radar control were established over the sea.

While the first generation of post-war aircraft was pitting its strength against the challenge of the sound barrier, plans were being made to exploit the knowledge gained. The problems of control were capable of solution but not by relying on human strength and response alone. Power assistance to the pilots' efforts was needed and powered controls had been under investigation for some time but in Britain their application to experimental aircraft was somewhat delayed and their development is a story in itself.

By 1955 the fruits of Britain's early transonic research were nevertheless being gathered as squadrons of home-produced swept wing jet fighters started to enter Royal Air Force service, but having been a long time coming they were no advance on the best that other nations possessed. Two old rivals for the world's speed record, the Supermarine Swift and the Hawker Hunter single-seat fighters, both found a place in the new look Fighter Command, although the Swift, which had been hastily ordered as a back-up for the Hunter, became the subject of a bitter cancellation decision culminating in the type being reallocated to Fighter Reconnaissance duties which in the end it performed most admirably. In the meanwhile two significant aircraft had made their first flights. One of these, the twin jet English Electric P1, after starting life as an experimental machine was eventually developed into the Lightning fighter, which became the first truly supersonic aircraft (i.e., capable of flying faster than sound in level flight) to join the Royal Air Force. The other, the Fairey FD.2, of which only two were built, was a small, delta wing, research aircraft with a long 'needle' nose and an extremely thin wing. The FD.2 flew into fame on 10 March 1956, when, piloted by Peter Twiss, a Fairey Aviation Limited test pilot, it raised the world air speed record to 1132 miles/h (a massive 30 per cent increase on the existing, American held, record), this being the first occasion on which this record had been raised to above 1000 miles/h. At a later date an FD.2 was fitted with a wing shape similar to that of the Concorde airliner and gave valuable service by investigating the flight characteristics to be expected with the full-size aircraft. This conversion, undertaken by the British Aircraft Corporation, was allocated their type number 221.

In the early 1950s visitors to the then annual Society of British Aircraft Constructors show at Farnborough were treated, when the weather permitted, to an abundance of supersonic bangs during the traditional afternoon flying displays, and as year after year the crowds flocked to see the progress being made by British aviation they revelled in each noisy demonstration of high-speed flight. The most sensational events were usually provided by the smaller experimental and fighter type aircraft but from 1952 onwards some impressive developments in large aircraft attracted the attention of the more discerning. A trio of bombers, the Valiant, the Vulcan, and the Victor, began to be demonstrated in dignified displays which, if not generating the breathless tension of their smaller brethren, nevertheless suggested awesome power, and although none of these V-bombers, as they became known, was specifically designed to fly at supersonic speeds, one of them, the Victor, did once dive faster than sound and all flew well into the transonic region during normal operations. In doing so they built up the experience of multi jet aircraft operation that enabled British aircraft, engine, and component manufacturers to participate in jet airliner development to the extent that the VC.10, the last aircraft to be designed by Vickers-Armstrongs (Aircraft) Limited before becoming part of the British Aircraft Corporation, was, until Concorde, the only four jet transatlantic airliner to have been constructed other than by the 'superpowers' of America and Russia.

What of the engines which made supersonic flight possible? From the earliest days of British jet engine development it had been realized that the highest degree of co-operation between aircraft and jet engine designers would be desirable. In piston-engined installations the propulsive power was provided by a propeller forcing air back over the aircraft exterior. With jet engines on the other hand the thrust to give forward motion was derived from a huge quantity of air travelling at great speed inside the aircraft structure. As the overall efficiency of the engine depended to a large extent upon how easily this air could enter, traverse, and leave the system, aerodynamics came to be as important internally as it always had been externally. This led to many arguments between airframe and engine designers as any failure or apparent loss of engine performance found each blaming the other. The development of engine air intakes and ducts in fact became a science of its own and today accounts for a high percentage of the total effort, but engine research and development was initially hampered by the lack of suitable flying test beds. Examples of various piston-engined aircraft such as the Wellington and Lancaster were therefore converted to partial jet power and were, in consequence, endowed with a performance undreamed of when first built. (Photographs 4a and b.)

The arrival of a totally new aerodynamic problem together with a radically new type of engine produced a massive manpower requirement and this in turn meant new office, factory, and particularly airfield facilities. It also opened up a new era of test flying and at this stage it would perhaps be appropriate to mention an organization which has

Photograph 4a. Lancaster Bomber with Rolls-Royce Nene jet engines fitted in place of outboard Merlin piston engines.
(Rolls-Royce)

Photograph 4b. Lincoln Bomber fitted with Rolls-Royce Derwent jet engine beneath fuselage. Reheat was included in this installation.
(Rolls-Royce)

played a dominant part in British aviation, particularly during the embryo years of supersonic flight. This is the Empire Test Pilots School, at present situated within the Aeroplane and Armament Experimental Establishment at Boscombe Down, just north of Salisbury in Wiltshire.

The enormous expansion of flight testing activity after the outbreak of World War II created a comparable demand for test pilots and, by 1941, it had become clear that the operational pilots who had to do this work would learn the job more quickly with special training. In consequence a test pilots school was established at Boscombe Down in 1943 and the first course, consisting of two Royal Navy and eleven Royal Air Force officers, was completed early in 1944. (Photograph 5.) In 1945 the school moved to Cranfield in Bedfordshire, later the home of the new College of Aeronautics, and in 1947 a further move took place to the RAE, Farnborough. Having sojourned at Farnborough for twenty-one years and become almost a permanent feature of the town, the school then returned to Boscombe Down in 1968 when the airfield at Farnborough became unsuitable for intensive test flying. Responsible for imparting the higher flying skills and technical competence to so many British and other pilots the school quickly gained a reputation for professional expertise second to none and the brunt of the supersonic struggle was borne by graduates of the early courses.

At present, over thirty years after its foundation, the school remains among the most highly rated in the world and the prosperity of the British aircraft industry has owed much to the quality of its work, but this has been achieved only by maintaining a high standard of instruction, which in turn depends on more advanced aircraft being provided when the modification of existing types ceases to be an adequate substitute for modernization.

The story of supersonic flight is thus a thing of many parts and, in the following chapters, we describe Britain's aviation efforts in the 'sonic years'. Several 'firsts' can be claimed and whilst the recording of 'firsts' is a practice often derided in both technical and historical circles a note of such events is made when appropriate. If nothing else it indicates the wide scope of work undertaken by British pilots, engineers, and others in overcoming first the sound barrier itself, then the effects of heat generated by flying at over twice the speed of sound, and finally in promoting commercial supersonic flight in the shape of Concorde.

Before going into the detail of what we have just read, we must,

Photograph 5. The first Empire Test Pilots' School Course, 1943–44, taken on a visit to the Bristol Aeroplane Company. Back row: *Left to right:* F/Lt K. J. Sewell, DFM, W/Cdr G. V. Fryer, AFC, Mr E. A. Swiss *(Test Pilot, Bristol AC)*, S/Ldr M. W. Hartford, DFC, S/Ldr D. W. Weightman, DFC. Middle row: Mr I. Llewellyn Owen *(Bristol AC)*, S/Ldr A. K. Cook, DFC, S/Ldr J. C. Nelson, AFC, F/Lt R. V. Muspratt, DFC *(Eagle Squadron)*, F/Lt J. C. S. Turner. Front row: Lt G. P. L. Shea-Simmonds, RNVR, W/Cdr P. H. A. Simmons, DFC, W/Cdr S. Wroath, AFC *(Commandant)*, Mr A. J. Pegg *(Test Pilot, Bristol AC)*, Lt-Cdr G. R. Callingham, RN, Mr G. Maclaren Humphreys *(Chief Technical Instructor)*, S/Ldr H. G. Hazelden, DFC. *(Absent: W/Cdr P. F. Webster, DSO, DFC)* (A & AEE Boscombe Down – Crown Copyright)

however, explain the nature of the sound barrier in simple terms and we start by considering the root of all the problems – compressibility.

Imagine that you are walking towards a densely packed crowd of people; they see you coming; they have time to move out of the way and you walk through without effort. However, if you run, the people have little time to move; you crash into them; you compress them together and need a lot of muscle power to keep on running by forcing the people violently to one side or another – or in aerodynamic terms the crowd exerts a high drag.

The difference between these two crowd situations illustrates the difference between subsonic and supersonic flight. Subsonic flight is like walking and supersonic flight is like running – into a crowd of air molecules. But how can air molecules see an aeroplane coming? The answer is they don't 'see', they feel – they feel pressure pulses. When any object moves in air it gives a push to the layer of air molecules immediately next to its front surfaces, the first layer pushes the second and so on. The succession of pushes is called a pressure pulse and when pressure pulses strike the human ear they produce the sense of sound. Pressure pulses travel through air at 760 miles/h at sea-level and this is why this particular speed is called the speed of sound. If an aeroplane flies at less than 760 miles/h the pressure pulses have time to move ahead of the leading edges; they push the air out of the way and reduce the drag. For this reason aeroplanes were able to attain speeds of over 500 miles/h with the comparatively low power of piston engines. (NOTE: The speed of sound changes with air temperature. In the colder air at high altitude it is only 660 miles/h.)

Now consider what happens when the aeroplane flies at, or above, the speed of sound. In this case the pressure pulses, being unable to go faster than 760 miles/h, cannot move ahead of the aeroplane; they cannot warn the air that something is coming; the air, like the crowd, is suddenly compressed; the aeroplane feels a very large drag and only a very large thrust will maintain the flight speed; the thrust, say, of a jet-propulsion engine. The change from uncompressed to compressed air takes place very suddenly across a very small distance, the boundary between the two conditions being the shock wave, seen in Photograph 1.

So at first both for ballistic missiles and for aeroplanes the sound barrier was just another, and perhaps unfortunate, name for extra drag (attributed to W. F. Hilton at the National Physical Laboratory), but that was where any similarity between the two ended. The aeroplane, unlike the missile, needed wings to produce lift, it needed controls to produce the changes of lift for manoeuvre, it needed suction over the wing to produce this lift, suction was the opposite of compression and compression occurred at the speed of sound. In other words, the sound barrier destroyed lift but worst of all it did so in a way that at first was not easily predictable nor always repeatable. This uncertainty therefore put human life at risk and the risk came before aeroplanes could move at anything like the speed of sound for a reason we must now understand.

Wings produce lift mainly because their top surfaces are curved. The curvature accelerates the airflow just as river water accelerates when flowing past a stone; the acceleration produces suction so the wing lifts. In this way the air can be accelerated to the speed of sound when the aeroplane as a whole moves perhaps at only half this speed, so compression builds up and, even if this affects only a fraction of the wing surface, a significant loss of lift and rise of drag is produced.

One way to delay compressibility is therefore to have a small surface curvature but this can imply a very thin wing which, to remain rigid, has to be of small span. So at one time it seemed that if supersonic drag were to be overcome it might be with small wings giving sufficient lift at high speeds but not at the low speeds necessary for take-off and landing. The options were then a dangerously high landing speed or some extreme and expensive form of high lift device over and above existing devices such as simple flaps.

Such was the complexity of the problem, however, that progress on all fronts could not be expected and at first it was perhaps natural to concentrate on the recognizable problem of drag reduction. One approach was to try and make the air flow smoothly over a much greater area of forward wing surface than hitherto thus delaying a flow breakdown into forms of drag producing turbulence. This ideal state, known usually as laminar flow, did in fact show great theoretical promise and hopes were entertained of major reductions both in compressibility and other forms of drag, but unfortunately laminar flow was and still is very difficult to create due to the need for a degree of surface smoothness almost impossible to maintain, so something more practical was required.

In the closing stages of World War II the sound barrier thus appeared to be impregnable but then it was discovered that the Germans had made a decisive aerodynamic breakthrough in the form of the swept wing and this, in effectively producing the low wing curvature needed to reduce compressibility, had reduced the rise in drag and made possible a substantial rise in speed without the need for substantially more powerful engines.

The principle was the same as walking up a hill by zigzagging across the slope; the distance to the top is greater, the speed up the hill is slower, but the hill appears to be less steep. So it was with the swept wing – the air was made to cross a longer but apparently lower slope, or curvature, from leading to trailing edge, it took longer to go the greater distance, the airspeed was effectively reduced by the reduced curvature and, compared with the straight winged layout, this allowed the aeroplane to fly to a much higher speed without some of the air accelerating locally to the drag producing speed of sound. The ratio of the air speed to that of sound is known as the Mach number (M), after Ernst Mach, an Austrian scientist, the critical Mach number (M_{cr}) being that at which compressibility first appears. As an example of what this can mean, an aeroplane with straight wings might generate small areas of supersonic flow when flying at only 70 per cent of the speed of sound; with swept wings this would not occur perhaps until 80 per cent – in other words, for the same engine power, the swept wing aeroplane would be much faster because the increase of drag would commence at a higher Mach number. (NOTE: As the speed of sound decreases with height, an aircraft travelling at, say, 650 miles/h, has a Mach number of 0·85 at sea-level, but 0·98 at high altitude.)

The first proposal for using a swept wing on supersonic aeroplanes was in fact made as early as 1935, and also by the Germans but for different reasons. Once an aeroplane reaches sonic speed the compression of air produces a large shock wave at the nose, similar, if it could be seen, to that from the bow of a ship, and as large and sudden changes of density and pressure occur across the wave these must not be allowed to touch the aeroplane surfaces, particularly those of the controls, otherwise violent changes of trim might result. The wing tips must not therefore project beyond the wave and the two ways of preventing this are to have a short, straight, wing or a wing with a large sweep-back, more highly swept perhaps than is needed for flight merely in the region of the speed of sound. If the straight wing was selected it would, of course, also have to be thin to prevent strong shock waves forming on the wing itself. There are thus two reasons for swept wings, one to make an aeroplane feel it is going more slowly and the other to protect it from the bow shock wave.

So much then for the origins of our story – we must now continue with the history, and we go back to the year 1943. At the Royal Aircraft Establishment, Farnborough, a Spitfire stands waiting to fly. New words have entered the everyday vocabulary of aircraft engineers – Mach number, compressibility, shock waves, and many more. Sound is about to take on an added significance.

2

AIMING HIGH

During the first two years of World War II transonic speeds had become not only possible but, to the belligerent powers, a necessity, and fighter aircraft were being designed which could easily exceed their critical Mach number in dives. Phenomena such as loss of control, severe vibration, or both were consequently reported by test and service pilots and there was no doubt that such major problems required systematic investigation. British aircraft engineers were particularly alive to the dangers and, in 1943, at the Royal Aircraft Establishment, Farnborough, began a series of airborne experiments which, as far as supersonic flight is concerned, marked the birth of controlled flight testing in this field. A specially prepared and instrumented Spitfire flown by determined pilots and controlled by a team of aerodynamicists and structural engineers was the means by which the early knowledge was obtained. Wartime secrecy, however, prevented any mention of these efforts at the time and they have never received full credit. An examination of the work is thus essential to this book, but first let us review briefly the theoretical and ground-based studies which preceded the commencement of in-flight research.

Prior to the early part of the twentieth century the motion of bodies in air at transonic and supersonic speeds had, as we have seen, been studied only in relation to the drag of ballistic missiles. The simple methods of measuring projectile performance used by Benjamin Robins and his immediate successors had, it is true, been superseded by the more advanced techniques of wind-tunnels, but, until the 1930s, there was no reason to investigate aircraft behaviour in the realm of compressibility. In the 1920s, Sir Thomas Stanton, of the National Physical Laboratory, had made some measurements of the pressure distribution over model wings in a small supersonic wind-tunnel, but these were isolated experiments, although of considerable interest. By 1935 the growth of aircraft speed had compelled the scientists and mathematicians of many countries to take a more active interest in supersonic problems and the Germans in particular were well to the fore in developing theories and suggesting practical shapes for flight in this new environment. Further British studies of the behaviour of high-speed aerofoils had been undertaken, much of it in relation to the tip speed of propellers, but wind-tunnel facilities were urgently required to experiment on aircraft models of reasonable size.

Towards the end of 1937 general plans were therefore prepared for a high-speed wind-tunnel to be installed at the Royal Aircraft Establishment, Farnborough. A maximum air speed of 600 miles/h was intended and construction of a model was started in March 1938. The original idea was to use this model to optimize the design but prevailing international tension made completion of the project all the more urgent. Work was started on the main tunnel without waiting for the outcome of model tests and it was officially opened on 6 November 1942 by the Rt Hon. J. J. Llewellyn, then Minister of Aircraft Production.

It was inevitable that much of the early work in this tunnel should be devoted to the development of prototype and existing aircraft rather than to fundamental research, this action being dictated by wartime priorities. Some advantage did, however, accrue from the situation, which, as we shall now see, indirectly enabled Britain to take a lead in transonic flight testing.

How did this come about? A critical situation had arisen in RAF Fighter Command in 1941 when German Air Force squadrons started to operate the new Focke-Wulf 190 fighter, which could out-perform the latest marks of Spitfire. The immediate British reply was more speed and height for the Spitfire by reducing airframe drag and by installing the more powerful Merlin 61 engine, a solution which gave rise to an aeroplane of value in transonic research. So, whilst the Germans, who were undoubtedly the early front runners in supersonic study, concerned themselves mostly with what happened above the speed of sound, the British, although appearing to progress more slowly, began to see that before manned supersonic flight became commonplace, at least one generation of transonic aircraft would have to be built. Research therefore tended to be concentrated in this region rather than in trying to leapfrog immediately to a much higher supersonic Mach number. It was acknowledged that existing wind-tunnels were inadequate for more advanced transonic measurement; in particular the tunnel walls affected the airflow over test

28

models in a way that had not been fully determined. Until time could provide the answers there was little alternative but to conduct airborne experiments and the dangers involved were by no means underestimated. What results were required?

First, the large increases in drag known to occur above the critical Mach number had to be more accurately evaluated. Second, and by far the most important, the effects of compressible airflow on stability and control needed to be assessed. It was, for instance, known that above the critical Mach number an aircraft would usually pitch nose down due to the loss of lift, and an enormous amount of research at first went into minimizing this effect. Third, and largely dependent on drag and control investigations, a knowledge of structural loads imposed during transonic flight was vital not only for future designs but also for the tests in progress.

In May 1943, flight trials were commenced by the pilots and technical staff whose mandate was to learn what they could by any means available. They were pioneers and thus had no comparable work on which to base their test techniques. How did they obtain their results?

Prolonged dives were conducted from high altitude, the height being necessary to give room both for acceleration to speed and for pull-out. As a bonus the speed of sound was about 100 miles/h less at the starting height than at sea-level, so the aeroplane did not have to go so fast to achieve a given Mach number. An added advantage was that structural loads and control forces were very much lower in the rarefied upper air. Initially a Mustang Fighter of American design was used but this possessed only single-stage engine supercharging and could not attain an altitude greater than 28 000 ft. Some useful information was obtained but to make the exercise really worth while much greater starting heights were required to build up speed. A Spitfire PR Mark XI was consequently prepared for the main task (Photograph 6). It was eminently suitable being capable of climbing to 40 000 ft for high-altitude photography largely as a result of aerodynamic refinement, and, furthermore, possessed a thinner wing than any of its contemporaries. This meant that the airflow over the wing suffered less severe changes in direction than occurred on other similar aircraft, and provided all went well, the Spitfire was likely to reach Mach numbers higher than could be attempted by any other machine.

It is of interest to note here that in the early days of the Spitfire design some evidence from wind-tunnel tests at the National Physical Laboratory had suggested that a high-speed wing did not need to be as thin as that

Photograph 6. Artist's impression of Supermarine Spitfire PR XI diving at over 90 per cent of the speed of sound during tests at the Royal Aircraft Establishment, Farnborough, 1943–44.
(Colin Wilson)

intended by R. J. Mitchell for the Spitfire – the attraction of a thicker wing being stiffness and less difficulty with the fitting of equipment.

There was at the time, however, some lack of experience in predicting from models the conditions for laminar or turbulent flow on full-sized aeroplanes, so the flight tests had the privilege of showing conclusively that thin wings were the way to get near the speed of sound.

To those concerned with the trials one unpalatable fact had of course to be faced – the pilot's chances of escape in the event of trouble were virtually nil. Not that these particular tests were unique in this respect, but the information it was hoped to extract certainly was, and more than a little luck was needed. In the end the degree of success was remarkable. What happened is best described by referring initially to an official report written at the time.

Describing the test technique this RAE report said:

. . . The dive angle was usually about 45°: the procedure was to dive steadily until maximum Mach number had been reached (this took about 11,000 ft. in all cases) then to continue for a few more seconds before starting a gentle (2–3g) pull-out. The following table summarises the dives made:

Aeroplane	Starting Height	Max. Mach Number	Pull-Out Height
Mustang	28,000 ft	0.80 at 17,000 ft	10,000 ft
Spitfire	32,000 ft	0.85 at 20,000 ft	10,000 ft
Spitfire	36,000 ft	0.87 at 25,000 ft	15,000 ft
Spitfire	40,000 ft	0.89 at 29,000 ft	20,000 ft

It is of course not possible to decide the Mach number directly from A.S.I. (i.e., Airspeed Indicator) and altimeter readings by inspection, and a Mach number meter was therefore fitted to indicate to the pilot when he had reached the maximum value. This was extremely useful on the Mustang, but as it was only calibrated to 0.80 it was off the scale during a good part of the Spitfire dives. As these were made later, however, it was possible to estimate sufficiently closely the altitude at which maximum M was expected.

Before commencing the dive the pilot was warned of the possibility of large trim changes in the nose-down direction and of the possible ineffectiveness of the elevator trimmer tab. He therefore trimmed into the dive at the beginning, but when the nose down change appeared, near maximum M, he made no attempt to correct on the trimmer, but held it by stick force alone. If this is physically possible, it appears to be a sound procedure in any similar tests. . . .

Before compressibility arrived to complicate matters, a dive had been simply a matter of pushing the elevators down by pushing the control column forward. The force to do the pushing was then removed by operating the trim tab which held the elevators down in the diving position. To pull out, the pilot simply pulled back on the control column and retrimmed when level.

However, compressibility changed the dive drastically. In this case, as Mach number at first increased, there was a loss rather than a gain of lift so the nose went down and the pilot found himself pulling instead of pushing to maintain the dive angle. It was now dangerous to use the trimmer because the lost lift could return quite suddenly when the Mach number decreased, as it did in the lower warmer air. The aeroplane might then pull-out very quickly if the elevator was already trimmed for pull-out and the pilot might not have time to prevent loss of control followed perhaps by structural failure. This sequence of events could of course be demonstrated in wind-tunnels. What could not easily be expressed in numbers was the time required by both aircraft and pilot to respond to control demands. Here was a factor of paramount importance which flight tests alone could evaluate.

It was known at the outset of the 1943 high Mach number trials that some aircraft, both British and American, had already been lost during dives in which transonic speeds had been achieved, but information on the relevant symptoms and methods of recovery were not generally available. Even if it had been, one wonders how many pilots, untrained in test techniques, would have dared to sit tight under the circumstances and wait for natural laws to take their course.

The role of the Spitfire trials is now seen in perspective. On the one hand scientific measurements of immense value were obtained and on the other flying techniques were worked out by trained test pilots, which could save the lives not only of service pilots but also of their civilian colleagues, whose responsibility was to develop even more advanced types. It is of interest to record that whilst the RAE staff were mounting their effort with the Spitfire a most useful document was compiled by the late George Bulman – then Chief Test Pilot of Hawker Aircraft Limited – which drew attention to the new problem of transonic flight. Entitled 'Piloting Techniques at Compressibility Speeds (Some Notes on What to Expect and How to Cope)', it set out in simple language the results of his own experience and observations. Bulman had been to America as the leader of a team of British test pilots whose purpose was to evaluate American aircraft destined for combat. Not surprisingly the British possessed the very knowledge of recent fighting which United States designers and test teams required to produce efficient warplanes. Among other things, however, it was found that certain American fighters when performing diving tests were subject to loss of control and severe vibration at high speeds. Bulman and his team were familiar with these signs of high Mach number onset from their own work and he considered that the dangers involved should be elucidated as a flight safety measure. Extracts from his report read:

. . . As was the case in the early days when the phenomena of the stall and spinning were unknown, it is felt that some guidance will be welcomed by pilots as to what may be expected (and this will vary with the different types of aircraft), the best methods of avoiding the compressibility range, and the control methods necessary for recovery . . .

32

The majority of recoveries from dives in which the aircraft was temporarily out of control through nose heaviness were made below 15,000 ft and by pulling hard on the stick and waiting for something to happen. This therefore seems the best technique: pull steadily, watch the altimeter, don't flap and don't expect anything much to happen until below 15,000 – 20,000 ft. . . .

Had conditions of peace prevailed, the Spitfire experiments, together with Bulman's report, would have been made into sensational news. It was unfortunate that war clouded the events with secrecy.

By the end of 1943 sufficient information had been analysed to enable a first report on the Spitfire and Mustang trials to be completed. It concerned the all-important measurements of drag and changes of trim at high subsonic speeds, so was issued in advance of some separate data on wing drag and pressure distribution.

Two salient facts emerged. First, the drag rise commenced at a much higher Mach number, and was less severe, than expected. (Hence, by way of a bonus, the Mach numbers reached were much above those believed possible on the Spitfire.) Second, both the drag rise and the predicted nose heaviness were initiated at the same Mach number. To help in understanding the events so far, Figs. 2–4 should now be considered. These have been prepared from actual test data.

Figure 2 is simply a time history of some of the quantities measured – in this case airspeed, height, and elevator angle. It can be seen that the dive lasted for about 1¼ min. This does not at first seem a lengthy period; but imagine sitting in a cramped cockpit diving earthwards at over 600 miles/h, not being quite sure what will happen – a minute or more can then seem never-ending! Figures 3 and 4, not being related to time, take on the more detached appearance of laboratory results. Both the drag rise (Fig. 3) and the onset of the nose heaviness (as represented by a marked change of elevator angle – Fig. 4) can be seen to commence at a Mach number of about 0·75. This value is roughly the critical Mach number, representing the lowest speed at which the airflow over some part of the aircraft reaches the speed of sound. The general shape of these graphs, drawn over a quarter of a century ago, is still familiar to present-day aircraft engineers. Extensive research has, it is true, gone a long way to eliminating the early dangers of transonic flight but there is always improvement to be made, particularly for civil use when economics have to be considered.

A description of any scientific experiment is incomplete without mention of the instruments by which measurements are made. Strangely

Time secs	Height feet	Speed miles/h	Mach number	Angle of dive degrees	'g'	Elevator angle degrees	Notes
0	39 690	274	0·408	8·6	0·82	4·6	Stick forward pushing
2·7	39 570	278	0·418	9·3	0·65	4·3	into dive.
5·4	39 480	291	0·436	10·3	0·70	4·7	Elevator down.
8·1	39 390	311	0·463	12·7	0·42	4·3	
10·8	39 150	341	0·512	13·9	0·28	4·4	
13·5	38 610	365	0·549	20·6	0·29	4·7	
16·2	37 900	403	0·600	29·5	0·54	5·5	
18·9	37 250	421	0·640	31·1	0·44	4·5	
21·6	36 310	456	0·688	33·3	0·77	4·7	
24·3	35 240	490	0·738	33·2	0·58	4·6	Stick pulled back.
27·0	34 180	521	0·785	33·7	0·57	4·6	Elevator moving up as high
29·7	32 840	559	0·840	35·4	0·43	4·4	Mach number causes nose
32·4	31 490	592	0·880	39·9	0·45	3·3	down trim change.
33·8	30 650	601	0·886	45·9	0·62	1·4	
36·4	28 820	606	0·891	46·2	0·73	0·8	Highest Mach number 0·891
39·2	27 240	601	0·880	46·8	1·42	0·2	
41·8	25 520	609	0·880	46·1	1·22	0·3	Recovering from dive. Mach
44·5	23 940	598	0·864	31·4	1·85	0·2	number decreasing but stick
47·2	22 890	587	0·841	23·0	2·12	2·7	held back to start dive pull-out.
50·0	22 030	574	0·820	17·2	2·11	3·6	Stick now forward to prevent
53·6	21 380	561	0·801	12·7	1·52	3·6	nose rearing up and applying
56·6	20 850	548	0·783	10·5	1·21	3·8	too much 'g'.
59·4	20 500	541	0·756	7·3	1·33	4·3	
62·0	20 240	522	0·740	5·7	1·20	4·1	
64·7	20 080	510	0·730	4·7	1·19	4·1	Final levelling out
67·5	19 970	497	0·706	3·1	1·13	4·1	from dive.
70·1	19 880	477	0·676	1·7	1·03	4·1	
72·9	19 830	472	0·672	0·8	0·90	4·3	

NOTE: Highest speed reached 609 miles/h.

Temperature at start of dive −59°C (40 000 feet)

Temperature at end of dive −14°C (20 000 feet)

This was not a vertical dive. Maximum diving angle about 47°.

Figure 2. Spitfire – typical high-speed dive. Variation of measured quantities with time.

enough this vital aspect of the job is sometimes treated with indifference by engineers, who expect instruments to perform beyond the bounds of their capabilities. The early researches into transonic flying permitted no such liberties, however, and the whole success of the job, depending as it did on good fortune, could not be further jeopardized by careless

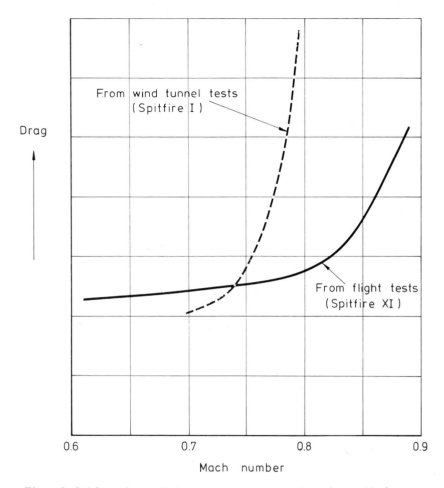

Figure 3. Spitfire – drag at high speed (note large rise in drag above a Mach number of about 0·8 during flight tests).

measurement. Many new problems presented themselves, the most difficult being the measurement of airspeed and height from which the all-important quantity of Mach number was computed. There were two main sources of error in determining these quantities. The first arose due to the presence of compressible airflow at high Mach numbers and the second from the need to dive at high rates of descent. An aircraft is surrounded totally by air and depends on the measurement of air pressure to determine its speed and height, so the changes in pressure introduced by compressible flow showed up as errors in the airspeed indicator and altimeter. In 1943 not only was the magnitude of these errors difficult to predict theoretically but, to make matters worse, no proved method of evaluating them existed. As if this wasn't enough, the rates of descent achieved in the dives (approximately 20 000 ft/min) introduced high degrees of lag in the pipes and mechanical parts comprising the speed and height measuring systems. In other words, at any speed and height, the

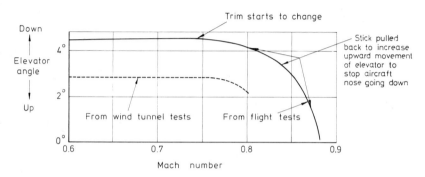

Figure 4. Spitfire high-speed diving tests. Change of trim at speeds near the speed of sound.

airspeed indicator, and to a greater degree the altimeter, couldn't keep up with the rapid changes inflicted on them. Laboratory tests to some extent served to evaluate the lag errors. Attempts to assess the corrections due to compressibility were made by diving past a specially calibrated Lancaster bomber and comparing altimeter readings at the instant of passing. Later methods employed radar tracking but in either case the most meticulous computation was necessary to arrive at an answer. Even today, after many years' experience of flight test techniques, the measurement of airspeed and altimeter pressure errors needs considerable care at any speed and not just at high Mach numbers.

Mention was made of a Mach number meter (subsequently to become known as a Machmeter) being fitted in aircraft engaged on high-speed trials. Developed by the instrument engineers at the RAE, this was the first of its type in the world, emphasizing, as probably nothing else could, the profound changes that were entering the aeronautical scene.

High-speed flight trials with Spitfires of various marks, and with other types, continued at the RAE throughout 1943 and 1944. They were not without incident but little by little more was learned not only of transonic flight but also of the methods necessary to obtain results. Equally important, increasing numbers of scientists and pilots were gaining invaluable experience in these fields. Looking back to the events of the time, Air Commodore A. H. Wheeler, who in 1943, as a Group Captain, was Officer Commanding Experimental Flying at the RAE, had this to say in a letter to the author:

I do remember, just before I left, taking a very serious interest in what we were doing because of the danger and I had a long talk with Thom and Mair (then Dr. Thom and Flight Lieutenant Mair, and now Professors Thom and Mair, respectively: the former retired and the latter at Cambridge University), and it was after these talks that I asked them to produce a height, speed and Mach number graph which I issued to all those who might be diving aeroplanes to very high speeds.

Perhaps an interesting side-light of all this is that during the period July 8th to July 26th 1943 I attached myself to a New Zealand fighter squadron at Biggin Hill to see how they did their operations and during one of these operations when we were doing high cover from a height of about 37,000 ft. over Holland, we had occasion to dive rather steeply and I was astonished to see something over 400 miles an hour on the airspeed indicator when we must still have been above 30,000 ft. There was probably an enormous position error and possibly compressibility error on this but when we had all pulled out again I did record in my mind, and recorded when I got back to Farnborough, to those concerned, that the people in fighter squadrons seemed to be already well ahead of us in high Mach number tests.

(AUTHOR'S NOTE: Spitfires and other aircraft at that time generally had an underwing pressure tube from which airspeed and height were derived and the position of this tube could cause a gross over-reading of speed particularly as Mach number increased. For this reason the RAE experimental high-speed Spitfires had a new pressure tube installation on the leading edge of the wing which gave much smaller errors.)

From the scientific side Mr W. J. Charnley (at present Controller of Research and Development Establishments and Research, Ministry of Defence, and who in 1943 was a co-author of reports on the high-speed trials, an extract from which has just been given) retains the following memories of these activities:

I arrived at the R.A.E. in January 1943 and soon became involved in high speed aerodynamics. At that time the Gloster–Whittle experimental jet aircraft commanded much attention and the more senior people devoted their efforts mainly to this project.

The more junior of us looked after the Spitfire but it soon became apparent that far from being a 'second team' job this series of tests was of paramount importance to high Mach number study.

We had many moments of excitement and humour. On one occasion when Martindale had suffered a shattered supercharger he landed at Worplesdon (near Guildford). He rang from a local pub where we subsequently found him in the bar having safely extracted the all important instrumentation cameras from the aeroplane.

To calibrate the airspeed and altitude instruments I sat freezing in the rear turret of a special Lancaster past which the Spitfire dived at 25,000 ft. A radio link operated instruments in both the Lancaster and Spitfire simultaneously.

(NOTE: The test pilot Martindale, mentioned in the above text, was in civil life a Rolls-Royce pilot. After war service in the Royal Air Force he returned to civil test flying but unfortunately died in 1955.)

On an earlier occasion Martindale had experienced similar damage but had managed to land back at the RAE. Photographs 7a and 7b show his aeroplane (Serial No. EN.409) before and after this flight. In the second picture the propeller can be seen to be missing and also part of the nose structure.

In 1946, over two years after Martindale's magnificent efforts, a meeting was held between senior RAE and Supermarine personnel to discuss the experience so far gained on flight tests at high Mach numbers (present were Messrs Morien Morgan, Handel Davies, and W. J. Charnley of RAE; Messrs A. N. Clifton, E. Mansbridge, and S. R. Hughes of Supermarine), and a report of the outcome (Supermarine Technical Office Report No. 4809) was written by Mr Clifton which makes a fitting epilogue to the whole Spitfire saga. Among other things it was stated that out of fifteen aeroplanes dived into the transonic region, 'the Spitfire is the only case where drag was the limiting factor, nose down trim change being apparent though not decisive at the height of test. On other types, fore and aft pitching, nose down trim change and buffeting were limiting features. On several American types tested in USA, aileron "buzz" (high frequency vibration of ailerons and system) has proved a limit. The ailerons move through fairly large angles and there is danger of structural failure.'

Photograph 7a. Squadron Leader Martindale's Spitfire PR XI before high-speed dive.

Photograph 7b. The same aircraft after damage during dive. The propeller is missing and part of the nose structure.
(Royal Aircraft Establishment – Crown Copyright)

Supermarine had in fact just begun to test their first jet-propelled aeroplane – eventually known as the Attacker (first flew 27 July 1946) – so they had an immediate interest in the proceedings. Perhaps even more interesting is Table 1, which shows the maximum Mach numbers achieved by these aeroplanes.

Table 1

Aeroplane	Jet = J Piston = P	Mach No. reached in flight tests	Limiting factor
Mustang I	P	0·79	Longitudinal oscillation
Mustang III	P	0·82	Trim change porpoising
Spitfire XI	P	0·9+	Propeller efficiency and elevator trim change
Spitfire IX	P	0·85	(Not stated)
Spitfire XXI with guns	P	0·8 (Not max. obtainable)	Buffeting
Spitfire XXI without guns	P	0·88	Drag rise propeller efficiency
Tempest V	P	0·85	(Not stated)
Welkin I	P	0·7	Loss of lift
Vampire I	J	0·8	Longitudinal oscillation
E28/39	J	0·82	Buffeting
Meteor I	J	0·8	Buffeting
Meteor I with long nacelles	J	0·84	Elevator trim change

It can be seen that the Spitfire XI exceeded, by a handsome margin, the Mach number attained by the best of the other types, even including the jets. Had it been fitted with an extra source of power (rocket ?) it might then have been able to achieve this performance in level flight giving more time for test observation than when diving.

Once the Spitfire experiments had shown the way, designers began to think even more of the low drag possibilities of laminar flow. The maintenance of laminar flow was not, however, easy; the smallest surface imperfection such as a squashed insect, the scratch from a stone or a dent on the outer skin being sufficient to cause turbulence, and for test purposes numerous tricks were tried. Brown paper was used to cover specially smoothed wing surfaces during take-off and climb, the paper being pulled off when the aircraft was high enough to be clear of insects. Substantial reductions of drag were in fact obtained by keeping the wings smooth in this way but the technique was obviously not suitable for everyday use; certainly not for military operations. One unique proposal

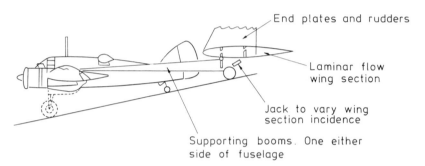

Figure 5. Beaufighter with proposed laminar flow wing section mounted on booms attached to wings. Angle of test wing to airflow could be changed by a jack.

was to mount a large 'trailer' wing of 40 ft span behind a Beaufighter aircraft (Fig. 5) for drag tests on near full-size laminar flow wing sections but this was never flown.

There was, however, another, more immediately practical, way of achieving low drag, or so it seemed, and this involved reducing the area of drag-producing surfaces; for instance by doing away completely with the tail. Tailless aeroplanes were not without precedent and some had flown in the pioneer days but these had been both small and of very low performance. Studies of tailless aeroplanes showed, however, that their small control leverage could not easily counteract a large change of trim arising from the operation of a leading or trailing edge high lift device, and this meant that some extra wing area was required for landing to compensate for the lack of flap. Now this extra area produced drag which simply replaced the drag of the surfaces removed from the tail, so for small high-speed aeroplanes there was little chance of reducing drag substantially by adopting the tailless layout. But this did not necessarily mean the end of the flying wing, for its extra wing area suited the requirements of the larger, load-carrying, bomber and transport aircraft, and to this end tailless research not only continued but was formalized by the setting up of a group known as the Tailless Aircraft Advisory Committee. As with most such organizations this Committee consisted of representatives from both government and industry, the first meeting being held in the office of the Director of Scientific Research, Ministry of Aircraft Production, Thames House, London, on 10 September 1943. The aims of the Committee had been set out in a letter to the Secretary of the Society of British Aircraft Constructors, the first paragraph of which is quoted below.

In order to provide information on the tail-less and tail-first aircraft, a research programme is being inaugurated which will consist of the construction of small full-scale aircraft as well as model tests. It is desirable that the designs of the aircraft, which will be about one-third scale models of large aircraft, should approximate as closely as possible to actual full-scale designs. To assist in this it is proposed that an Advisory Committee be formed consisting of representatives of M.A.P. Headquarters, R.A.E., N.P.L., and aircraft firms. It is desired to keep the Committee as small as possible and to restrict it to people who can make technical contributions of value in the development of these types.

No tailless aircraft of over 6000 lb weight had at that time been flown and extensive experimental work was needed to undertake with confidence the design of a much larger machine, so it was decided to build several tailless gliders as a simple and cheap means of conducting flight tests. This work was therefore put in hand and was in progress when the war ended, but on 20 April 1945, at the sixteenth meeting of the Tailless Advisory Committee, the German work on swept wings was revealed for the first time when it was noted briefly that:

. . . a German report stated that on the basis of the critical Mach No. occurring at about $3 \times$ low speed drag, tunnel tests gave the critical Mach No. for a sweep back of $40°$ to be 0.95 compared with 0.83 for a straight wing. . . .

As we now know the use of sweepback sounded the death-knell of the flying wing layout as such, but in 1943, with the future by no means certain and with flying wing research only in its infancy, the study of supersonic flight was bound to be centred on more conventional layouts.

As the eagerly awaited results of the Spitfire high Mach number tests were being studied, a chain of events was set in motion which ultimately led to one of the most controversial decisions in the history of British aviation. Not far from Farnborough and adjacent to Reading, lies the town of Woodley, home at the time of Miles Aircraft Limited, and in October 1943 this company was awarded a contract to design and build an experimental aircraft capable of supersonic flight. Having an official specification number E24/43, the project is perhaps better remembered by the firm's type number M52, but, either way, when first conceived it seemed extremely bold and quite in keeping with the idea of 'Britannia' ruling at least a part of the air. Little was then known, of course, of the advanced stage of German research. In America some excellent wind-tunnels existed, few jet engines were available, and although some of their fighter aircraft had experienced compressibility troubles these had not then been systematically studied. The British had performed compara-tively meagre theoretical and wind-tunnel work but knew more about jet engines and about manned transonic flight experiments than the rest of the world put together.

In short, the British first team was undoubtedly strong but were the reserves sufficient to warrant aiming for such a goal as speeds well in excess of Mach 1? It was partly on this issue that the Miles M52 was eventually cancelled before it flew but this does not detract from its merit or interest. Many ill-informed statements adorn its history so let us examine the proposals in detail.

The success of the undertaking in fact depended mostly on the development of a suitable engine. There is no doubt that when the Specification was first issued the thrust available from the most powerful jet engine was insufficient to propel an aircraft of the necessary size at anything like supersonic speed in level flight. The Spitfire tests, although highly successful, had shown that diving was a most undesirable way of obtaining results, from the aspects of safety, the limited time available, and the rapidly changing conditions. Level, or near-level, flight at $M=1$ or greater was thus a prime requirement for the M52. Plans were therefore laid to increase the engine thrust and, if needs be, to use an external jettisonable, bi-fuel rocket of German origin. One way of increasing thrust was with reheat (or afterburning), a system in which fuel was burnt in the jet pipe in addition to the normal burning in the combustion chamber. This provided about 30 per cent of extra thrust and, of course, a very large increase in fuel consumption, but if needed only for short periods, it was very convenient.

Preliminary designs for the M52 were prepared and some theoretical studies undertaken at the RAE. It is of interest to note here that before the first results of the Spitfire tests had been formally reported they were used to assist in calculations for the M52. A quick dividend was thus paid.

In December 1943 an RAE report was published, entitled 'Note on the Miles Supersonic Aircraft (Preliminary Version)'. It was classified MOST SECRET and contained the following statements:

> The top speed in level flight at 36,000 ft. of the preliminary version of the Miles Supersonic Aircraft will be about 600 m.p.h. It should reach supersonic speeds in level flight if a short period increase in thrust is provided to accelerate from 600 m.p.h. to 1,100 m.p.h., e.g., by diving or by rocket assistance.
>
> . . . the thrust required around the speed of sound could be provided by a bi-fuel rocket, arranged to be jettisoned as in the take-off rocket apparatus now being developed. A unit providing a thrust of 5,000 lb for 25 seconds would be suitable; it would weigh 1,500–2,000 lb. Such a unit is already available (Aerojet XZS ALD-6000).
>
> Although assistance in this manner will be essential to some degree, it is clear that the amount required should be kept to a minimum, e.g., that the greatest possible thrust should be demanded from the main engine and that the drag of the aeroplane should, if possible be reduced still further by decreasing wing thickness.

The engine requirements were influenced by a factor not often appreciated when appraising British experimental aircraft designs, namely, the local geographical and meteorological situation. A high percentage of take-offs and landings from British airfields involve hazards such as bad visibility, low cloud, rain, and haze (the landing phase in particular being a critical operation for high-performance machines possessing low fuel reserves). Even if large airfields with comprehensive approach aids are available the risks can still be high. The M52 was being designed to fly at a time when Britain possessed few concrete runways of the size common today (i.e. 9000 to 12 000 ft long).

The Aeroplane and Armament Experimental Establishment at Boscombe Down, just north of Salisbury, had 9000 ft, but a new runway in the north–south direction was about to be built and the paraphernalia of construction works would litter the eastern end of the main landing area. The RAF emergency airfields at Woodbridge in Suffolk, Carnaby near

Bridlington, and Manston in Kent were of a similar size to Boscombe Down, but the nature of their operations at least until 1945 precluded their use for flight testing. Thus any possibility of operating, say, a purely rocket-powered version of the M52 dropped from a parent machine in the manner later envisaged by the Americans was initially out of the question, at least from a home base. The landing, without power at high speed after the rockets had burnt out, would have needed a guarantee of cloudless skies and very long landing strips away from populated areas. Such a combined requirement just could not and never will be met in the British Isles. So the plans for landing an M52 had therefore to be based on having not only engine power available but also a reasonable reserve of fuel. Some members of the Miles design team had in fact proposed carrying the M52 aloft beneath a Lancaster bomber to save the fuel needed for take-off and climb, but this idea was not adopted. The operating mode for the Miles supersonic project was therefore as follows:

(1) To take off and climb rapidly to high altitude.

(2) To attain supersonic speed in either level flight or in a shallow dive.

(3) To possess sufficient reserves of fuel after climb and supersonic test run to ensure safe return to base and landing.

The amount of fuel to be carried obviously played a large part in determining the size and weight of the aircraft and hence its engine thrust requirements – not that there was really much choice of engine.

A Power Jets' W2/700 unit, which was a special version of the early Whittle engine, was developed for the M52, but this alone, even with reheat and other aids, was not going to deliver enough thrust for the job, and, as we shall see in Chapter 8, it was much more complex than anything previously designed or tested. A situation was now arising which has always been disliked by aircraft designers and test engineers alike, this being the mating of an advanced airframe with an equally advanced engine system. The problems of either occupy enough development time but together they can, if major snags arise, constitute a major and uneconomic risk.

As it seemed that the engine designers were going to have to fight hard for every ounce of thrust, what could be done on the aircraft side to ensure the maximum use of engine power? Two conflicting requirements here became apparent. First, because of fuel shortage, the aircraft wing had to be capable of lifting the M52 quickly to the great heights (in the 50 000 ft region) necessary for attaining high Mach numbers. Second, it was thought at the time that the wing had to be of thin, low drag sections giving also a high critical Mach number. The rate of climb was all important as it would be useless to expend so much fuel in reaching the test height that none was left for performing the tests and then landing. Unfortunately the thin wing sections thought necessary for high Mach number flight could not produce the degree of lift required for rapid climbing – at least not with the thrust then available, nor could they contain much fuel. How about using rockets to assist the climb? Possible, but external rockets were likely to be needed for accelerating to supersonic speeds and there was a limit to the number that could be carried bearing in mind the gear needed for jettisoning.

The Germans had, it is true, successfully produced a rocket fighter, the Messerschmitt Me.163, but this was a military machine of short, subsonic, endurance. It was also expendable, and in wartime losses were accepted whether in combat or otherwise. Expensive experimental machines are never produced in quantity and all possible precautions are taken to avoid accidents in order to obtain maximum return for financial investment. The Me.163, although a most praiseworthy technical achievement, cannot therefore be compared with the M52 specification.

By the end of 1943 preliminary design schemes for the M52 had been prepared, the proposed main dimensions of the aircraft being as follows:

Wing area   120 ft^2 (gross) 87 ft^2 (net)

Span   21·75 ft^2

Wing   7½% thickness/chord ratio
Symmetrical bi-convex section
Aspect ratio = 4

Overall length   27·5 ft

Fuselage max. diameter   4·8 ft

Tailplane area   27 ft^2 (net) 39·2 ft^2 (gross)

Fin and rudder area   28 ft^2

Empennage   7½% thickness/chord ratio

The all-up weight was estimated as 6500 lb including 2000 lb of fuel.
Drag and thrust calculations for a proposed test height of 36 000 ft

46

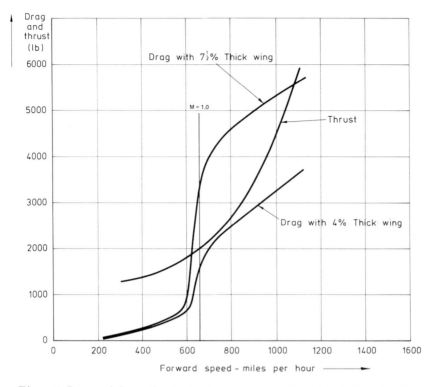

Figure 6. Drag and thrust of Miles M52 supersonic aircraft. Height: 36 000 ft. (Note marked reduction in drag with 4 per cent thick wing.)

showed that at speeds above 600 miles/h (M = 0·9) the total drag exceeded the available thrust, and thus supersonic speed could not be attained in level flight. If by some means, such as diving from about 60 000 ft or rocket assistance, the aircraft could be accelerated to 1100 miles/h then the thrust would start once again to exceed the drag, and level flight at very high Mach numbers might be sustained, this possibility being shown in Fig. 6. All this presupposed satisfactory engine handling and performance under completely unexplored conditions, but, as we shall see later, some time was to elapse before jet engine development reached the stage where reliable operation of thrust-augmented engines could be ensured above 35 000 ft.

One thing seemed obvious. In the absence of any other solution the wing thickness would have to be reduced considerably to effect a large decrease in drag. It was consequently decided to investigate the possibility of building a wing of 4 per cent thickness/chord ratio. Nothing approaching this figure had previously been attempted and the manufacturing difficulties were considerable. Flying control surfaces had to be attached and the whole structure had to be stiff enough to cope with aero-elastic effects in general and flutter in particular. Little enough was known about the mechanics of flutter to make this aspect of the M52 design alone a limiting factor on maximum speed but some risk could not be avoided.

The situation was well described by Professor A. R. Collar, a noted authority on aero-elasticity, during a lecture to the Historical Group of the Royal Aeronautical Society on 13 December 1977, when he said:

> In 1943 the chief technician of Miles Aircraft Limited appeared in my office to tell me, in the greatest secrecy, that his firm had been asked by the Ministry to build an experimental supersonic aircraft. It was to have straight wings, of lenticular (i.e. bi-convex) section, with a thickness chord ratio of 4 per cent. He said he must know, within three weeks, how stiff it had to be.

In the event a rough-and-ready analysis was available in the required time, but a complete study subsequently took two years!

Had the structural problems, however, been non-existent, the progress of engine development soon became a restricting factor in assessing the results which could reasonably be expected from the M52. In July 1944, when considerable advances in the design had been made, an RAE Technical Note, entitled 'Further Note on the Miles Supersonic Aircraft (E24/43)', was firmly of the opinion that the M52 had no hope of reaching supersonic speed in level flight. The size, all-up weight, and drag had increased over and above the original estimates (this being a common design *malaise*), and whilst performance estimates had been pessimistic in the past (for example, with the Spitfire), the much publicized 1000 miles/h target for the M52 was simply too far from the possible to be corrected by a dose of optimism. Only engine thrust could close the gap, and engine thrust showed no signs of being increased substantially in the short term. In this respect what was clearly needed was an engine having an axial flow compressor possibly possessing a smaller cross-sectional area than those of the proposed centrifugal compressor designs. A reduction in fuselage diameter and hence drag would have resulted. More thrust might also have been available but this could have involved an undesirable weight

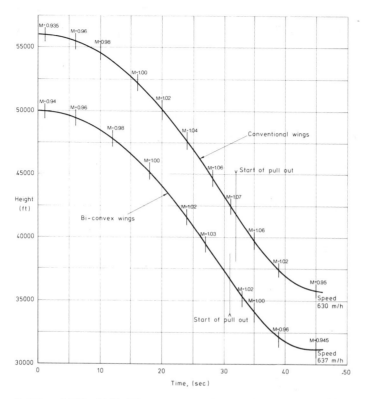

Figure 7. Dive of Miles M52. (Note greater starting height with conventional wing.)

increase. As it was, plans had to be formulated around the available rather than the promised.

In anticipation of having to accept a lower power/weight ratio than originally envisaged, design studies were produced of the aircraft's performance with a conventional wing section in place of the bi-convex type but having the same mean (7 per cent) thickness. These showed that whilst at supersonic speeds the drag of the bi-convex and conventional sections was roughly the same, the conventional wing offered a higher Mach number capability. This may at first sight seem surprising but the explanation is simple. The aircraft had to climb to its test altitude at subsonic speed when the conventional wing would give greater lift for a

49

given speed than could be obtained with the bi-convex section. Hence greater heights could be achieved at which higher Mach numbers would be possible. The air loads during dives in the less dense air would also be smaller and there were other advantages. First, the dive could be terminated at a greater height, giving more space for pull-out, and, second, the take-off performance could be improved. Features of the dives can be seen in Fig. 7 which is reproduced from an RAE Technical Note.

Figure 7 shows the expected height, Mach number, and time during typical 45 degree supersonic dives with the two wing sections mentioned, from which the comparison shown in Table 2 can be drawn.

Table 2

Section	Starting height (ft)	Pull-out height (ft)	Maximum Mach number
Bi-convex	50 000	32 000	1·03
Conventional	56 000	36 000	1·07

It will be seen that in a 45 degree dive the M52 would, in either case, have been only just supersonic provided the estimates of performance were substantially correct.

At an all-up weight of 7493 lb for which direct comparison is possible, the take-off distance to a height of 50 ft using a bi-convex wing would have been about 50 per cent greater than with a conventional section and would thus have consumed even more of the valuable fuel.

As time went by the Miles M52 thus tended to become aerodynamically a more conventional machine by the standards of the day. Only the cockpit layout gave it an appearance of being the 'super-plane' which some still unfairly believe it could have been.

What therefore might have been learned had it flown and how would it have fitted into the historical pattern of supersonic research? It must be remembered that the propeller-driven Spitfire had reached Mach numbers slightly over 0·9 and thus the M52 did not necessarily in its initial form represent a major step forward in terms of pure speed. Many accounts of problems associated with breaking the 'sound barrier' unfortunately give the impression that once an aeroplane of any sort had exceeded $M = 1$ then the way was open for all others. Nothing could have been further from the truth. A psychological victory would undoubtedly have been gained but the real need was not for a brute force effort to reach the maximum Mach number but rather to have sufficient reserve power both of engine and of control to advance in small steps through the transonic region with aircraft of differing wing layouts in order to measure thoroughly the stability and structural load changes taking place therein. The best overall shapes for supersonic aircraft had still to be evaluated in detail, so, initially, at least, the prime airframe requirement was for the lowest possible drag and freedom from buffet. It is possible therefore that the main contributions emanating from M52 transonic and supersonic flying would have been in the fields of powered flying controls, engine operation, and structural behaviour rather than in studying external shape. These three items represented most of what was new in dealing with problems of sonic speeds and above, as no matter what aircraft shapes might have emerged in an effort to reduce drag and buffet they still had to be controlled, propelled, and remain intact for all flight conditions.

Although destined not to fly, the M52 was undoubtedly the first aircraft in the world to be designed specifically for supersonic speeds. If completed would it have been the first actually to exceed $M=1$? This is an extremely controversial point and is really at the root of all criticism levelled at those who caused cancellation of the project. In 1946, the Americans had already commenced gliding tests on their Bell X-1 research aircraft but it was not until October 1947 that this machine made its historic faster than sound flight. Had the M52 been likely to fly in 1946 would the Americans have accelerated their X-1 programme and beaten the British contender for the supersonic crown? That they would have tried is almost certain as their more recent success in being first to the Moon amply emphasizes.

The Miles design team was naturally disappointed that its efforts on such an exacting specification as the M52 did not result in even one flight. Suggestions have been made that the Directors of the firm were relieved at the eventual cancellation of M52 as the difficulties attending such an advanced design looked like resulting in an embarrassing failure. Mr G. H. Miles himself, however (Photograph 8), has stated that this was not so and strenuous efforts were made right up to the end to keep the project alive. Was its cancellation justified?

Various reasons have been offered for cancelling the M52, but in 1946, at a press conference, Sir Ben Lockspeiser, then Chief Scientist to the Ministry of Supply, was reported as saying that manned supersonic

51

Photograph 8. The late Mr F. G. Miles and his brother, Mr G. H. Miles, with a wind-tunnel model of the Miles M52 supersonic aeroplane.
(Mr G. H. Miles)

research aircraft would, in the interests of pilot safety, be abandoned in favour of pilotless models. This statement was taken to mean particularly the Miles M52 and it has unfortunately been quoted as such on many occasions since 1946, notably by the denigrators of British policies. Does it really, however, stand comparison with the true situation? It was intended to fit the M52 with a pilot escape capsule as there was no room in the tiny cockpit for an ejector seat, but the design of these items was at the time in its infancy and it soon became obvious that the capsule would not be ready for early flight trials. The only means of escape would therefore have been by the traditional method of jumping out and releasing a parachute manually, but as the chances of getting out of any aircraft above a speed as low even as 300 miles/h were slim the M52 raised no new problem in this respect, and even the first two DH.108s flew without ejector seats despite an official desire to see them fitted.

It is therefore hard to believe that pilot safety was the overriding reason for cancellation but it is of interest here to note some remarks made by Mr R. Smelt in a lecture to the Royal Aeronautical Society on 9 October 1946 (Mr Smelt had been Head of Aero Flight (Jet) Section at the RAE during the war and was later Chief Scientist to the Lockheed Corporation of America). Describing some German proposals for a supersonic research aircraft, he commented: 'In fact, it appeared that much more ingenuity had been expended on problems of pilots' escape than on aerodynamics; possibly a wise step.' The main consideration, however, was that the research value of a machine should justify acceptance of a high accident potential. In other words, if an M52 had been lost early in the flying programme would sufficient have been learned of supersonic flight to render a satisfactory return for any outlay in money or lives? As it happened, the unexpected influence of German work soon entered into the deliberations of those concerned with directing British high-speed flight research, and when the rest of the world then began to share the German conviction of the value of swept wings for both transonic and supersonic speeds up to about $M = 1 \cdot 7$, there was little point in continuing the work on other layouts.

It seemed therefore that in continuing with the Miles M52 Britain might have become involved in undue expenditure and loss of life on a shape whose usefulness for the immediate future of transonic flight was open to question. The decision to cancel thus involved considerations of financial, technical, and safety aspects, and, in the end, although perhaps unfortunate for prestige, was not the drawback that some still imagine.

The British flew the first air-breathing-engined aircraft outside the USA to achieve supersonic flight (the de Havilland 108), produced the first commercial jet airliner (the Comet), achieved an overwhelming supersonic air speed record success with the Fairey Delta 2, and initiated the world's first operational supersonic airliner (Concorde). Moreover, the handling qualities of British high-speed aircraft have always been as good as and in many cases better than comparable foreign machines. More of this will be learned in later chapters but all these achievements should be remembered when tempted to exaggerate the effect of cancelling the M52.

If the firm of Miles had placed the name of Great Britain in the first place of supersonic achievement, an entry would duly have been made in the record book. This was not to be, but credit must still go not only to Miles for their efforts but also to the Ministry authorities responsible for envisaging, in wartime, the possibilities which the M52 was intended to realize.

There is never a clear-cut end to any story such as that of the M52. As a final word, therefore, mention is made of another Miles aircraft, the Falcon, to which was fitted experimentally an M52 wing shape together with a replica of an all-moving tailplane intended for flight on the

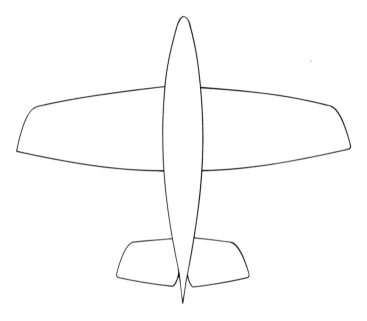

Figure 8. Plan view of Miles 'Gillette' Falcon – a low-speed touring aircraft used to test low-speed characteristics of wing for Miles M52 supersonic experimental aircraft.

supersonic aircraft. The Falcon, a light touring aircraft, had been used to test various wing shapes, and in the case of the M52 investigated the low-speed handling characteristics to be encountered during landing the full-sized aircraft. From the tests performed there was no reason to think that any severe problems would have been encountered in landing an M52. Thus the 'Gillette' Falcon, as it was known by analogy between its thin wing and a famous type of razor-blade, at least enabled something of the M52 to feel the hand of a pilot. A plan view of the aircraft is shown in Fig. 8.

Having described the M52 as an individual project the final question, however, must be asked. Did Britain really have an urgent interest in supersonic flight in the immediate post-war years?

The first clue to the answer probably lies in a series of documents known as the Fedden Report which described the visit of a British mission to America between December 1942 and May 1943. Led by the late Sir Roy Fedden, previously Chief Engineer of the Bristol Aeroplane Company, the aim of the mission was to enable British and American aircraft engineers to exchange knowledge and views in pursuit of their common war effort. The British team was, however, deeply impressed, if not disturbed, by the massive wartime growth of transport aircraft production in America which, when allied to an existing highly efficient air transport organization, was obviously going to give the Americans great advantages in post-war commercial aviation.

This prospect therefore rather than any thought of supersonic flight began to influence British policy, and whilst high speed was always a military requirement, any post-war military development was expected to be long term.

For this reason the first British swept wing jet aircraft, the de Havilland 108, was built primarily to promote a much larger jet-propelled transport, the requirements for which came from the Brabazon Committee, an organization set up in 1943 to decide post-war British air transport requirements. In this case transonic, rather than supersonic, flight became the first concern and British progress in this direction is described in the next chapter.

3

PLANS AND REALITY

At the end of World War II the vast fleets of fighting and transport aircraft possessed by the victorious nations became redundant almost overnight. Some of the combat machines, particularly the jet fighters, continued of course to meet a military need, and certain of the bombers and transports formed a nucleus for post-war civil aviation routes, but it was realized that the next decade would see the design of radically new aeroplanes powered by gas turbine engines. During the later war years and in the early days of peace popular magazines consequently carried artists' impressions of future aircraft, and if these did not represent in detail any particular type, at least they conveyed a feeling that an aviation Utopia was just around the corner.

The wartime achievements of British aircraft, coupled with the pioneering of jet-propulsion engines, did, moreover, leave no doubt in anybody's mind that Britain could make a substantial contribution to the growth of peacetime flying.

It would of course have been gratifying if, after six years of bloodshed, all forms of national activity could have proceeded at a chosen pace and in a predictable manner, but this was not to be. A wide ideological gulf still separated Communist Russia from her wartime allies to the extent that even before Germany had been defeated, fears were being expressed that fighting might follow a meeting of American and Russian troops on German soil. Russia had, after all, refused to recognize the exiled Polish government in Britain and had failed to assist the Warsaw liberation fighters, so the atmosphere was not exactly that of trust. It was even suggested later that the massive Royal Air Force raid on Dresden in February 1945 was intended not so much to accelerate the defeat of Germany as to deny to the Russians the only undamaged major base in Eastern Germany from which to mount operations against the West. Indeed, it was not long before the western powers were forced to undertake the historic Berlin airlift to counteract the Russian closure of supply roads into the ruins of the city.

The uncertainties of the post-war period thus ensured that jet propulsion would continue to develop at a rapid pace, but as the fuel consumption of jet engines would not for some time be low enough to satisfy the economics of commercial air transport, the way to higher performance was expected to be led by military aviation, in this case across the barrier of sound.

By the end of 1947 plans had therefore been laid for the re-equipment within ten years of both the Royal Navy and the Royal Air Force. At least one of the proposed aircraft was to be a fighter capable of exceeding the speed of sound by a large margin and an assumption was made that no major war would break out before 1957. The circumstances under which a start had to be made could not, however, have been much worse. In 1947 most of Britain suffered an appalling winter which caused a severe fuel crisis: major industrial undertakings had to close down, including the wind-tunnels on which so much depended, and even Royal Air Force airfields were forced to close through lack of heating facilities. The poor state of the economy after the war had in any case caused a slowing down of effort, and by 1950 British aviation was firmly in the doldrums. Successes such as the de Havilland 108, the export potential of jet-propulsion engines, and experience with the early generations of Meteor and Vampire jet fighters did, of course, do something to promote a range of newer aeroplanes, but only research could speed up the process and research was sadly lacking.

Then, in June 1950, came the Korean War, and the British were shocked to find that, from being a dominant aviation power with such machines as the Spitfire, Mosquito, Lancaster, and Halifax, they had lost their lead, particularly in fighter aircraft. The Americans, the Russians, and even a country as small as Sweden had quickly utilized captured German technology to develop swept wing fighters which decisively out-performed the Meteors and Vampires of the Royal Air Force first line squadrons. The Americans, in particular, had been piling up the super-sonic hours, and their methods of allocating research contracts through Air Force or Navy channels had generated an intense rivalry between the pilots of these two service branches. In the process of flying a wide range of supersonic research aeroplanes starting with the Bell X-1, both the US Air Force and the US Navy broke speed and height records and reached

Mach numbers which in 1945 had seemed many years away. Reports of these tests are of great technical interest and although a few of the test pilots' memoirs seem to dwell at length on the record-breaking aspects there is no doubt that many fears of flight beyond the sound barrier were dispelled by their efforts.

A leisurely re-equipment of British air power was of course now out of the question and something like panic ensued. Not only had existing plans to be accelerated but interim and unpopular plans had to be made, including the purchase of American fighters and bombers. A system known as 'Super-Priority' was devised to hasten home production of aircraft for immediate combat use and, in some cases, supersonic research had to be postponed in consequence.

By 1954 the worst was, however, over and an enormous re-expansion of the aircraft industry had produced a new generation of British transonic fighters. New heavy bombers were coming along and even several supersonic machines were on the way – but so were the rockets, and in 1957 a Government White Paper, produced under the direction of Mr Duncan Sandys, then Minister of Defence, appeared to sound the death-knell of the manned aircraft for first line squadron service. So, the new air force created in ten years, from 1947 to 1957, now seemed likely to be planned out of existence in favour of ballistic missiles.

In the next few chapters we therefore look at what was done and what was learned in these early peacetime years, starting in this chapter with the initial transonic research.

One of the most urgent requirements in 1945 was, in fact, for an aircraft research establishment with a large airfield. The existing runways at Farnborough were not only short but the approaches lay over populated areas. Tentative suggestions were made for joining Farnborough to the nearby wartime airfield at Blackbushe, but the proximity of the area to the growing London airport control zone was a serious operational hazard. Eventually a site just north of Bedford was selected, taking in the two wartime Royal Air Force airfields of Twinwood and Thurleigh.

The Government's intention to start the Bedford project was announced in 1945 by the late Sir Stafford Cripps, then Minister of Aircraft Production, who said:

. . . the Government has decided that it is necessary to embark upon the construction of a new research and development centre in this country in which all the latest and best wind tunnels and other apparatus can be installed.

After a very complete survey of the country, it has been decided to place the new research establishment in the vicinity of Bedford.

Originally known as the National Aeronautical Establishment (NAE), it is now called Royal Aircraft Establishment Bedford, and contains among other units a comprehensive wind-tunnel complex and the once Farnborough-based Aero Flight which is responsible for airborne experiments. To complete the conversion of Bedfordshire into an aviation county a College of Aeronautics was established at Cranfield and the industry staked its claim through the creation of the Aircraft Research Association, an organization sponsored by member firms to provide central wind-tunnel facilities, thus avoiding uneconomic duplication within the industry and providing smaller firms with access to equipment which alone they could not afford.

The formation of the College was recommended by the Aeronautical Research Committee on 10 August 1943, and Sir Stafford Cripps quickly set up a special committee to prepare proposals. Under the Chairmanship of Sir Roy Fedden this committee issued a report on 19 July 1944, which included the words:

> We are not charged with examining the case for such a College. We have taken it for granted.

The decisiveness of these wartime plans for peacetime aeronautics perhaps seems unfamiliar in the present era, but for the most part the plans were fulfilled. Behind the scenes, however, a somewhat less orderly contribution was made to this new British research capability. Known as Operation 'Surgeon' (i.e., carving out), it involved the removal of key German research equipment, with emphasis on supersonic flight, and its re-establishment in the British Isles. German scientists were also offered inducements to work abroad. The trouble was that the Americans, the Russians, and others had the same idea and some real 'cloak and dagger' work took place.

Particularly of interest were the recently constructed and well-concealed LFA (Luftfahrt Forschungsanstalt, Hermann Göring – Air Force Research Establishment) at Volkenrode, near Brunswick, and the older and internationally esteemed AVA (Aerodynamische Versuchsanstalt – Aerodynamic Research Establishment) in the famous university town of Göttingen – this unit being part of the Kaiser Wilhelm Institute.

The Chief Scientist of Operation 'Surgeon' was latterly the late Mr Jack

Hanson, then of the Ministry of Aircraft Production and whose subsequent appointments included Chief Superintendent at both Boscombe Down and RAE Bedford. Some notes left by Mr Hanson shortly before his untimely death in the spring of 1978 were partly intended for this book and he wrote:

> By British standards L.F.A. was outstanding for the size and scale of its facilities and for the efforts made to conceal an establishment covering a large area (2½ square miles). The staff included some of Germany's most outstanding scientists. In July 1945 A.V.A. at Göttingen also became part of operation 'Surgeon' and whilst Germany was not permitted by the allied powers to engage in military work, the A.V.A. was allowed to continue general aerodynamic research.

Mr Hanson and others in the 'Surgeon' team are shown in Photograph 9. They are standing outside the AVA.

Also concerned with Operation 'Surgeon' was Mr P. T. Fletcher, then Head of the Heavy Research Plant Section in the Ministry of Works, whose responsibility was the actual removal and re-installation of the machinery selected by the scientists. Mr Fletcher later became (in 1975) President of the Institution of Mechanical Engineers, and in his Presidential address made some reference to 'Surgeon', including these words:

> The planning of N.A.E. Bedford had started, and it was possible to design the 3 × 3 ft Mach 2 supersonic wind tunnel to incorporate twin centrifugal compressors . . . taken virtually unused from Volkenrode. The later 8 ft supersonic wind tunnel also incorporated other larger d.c. motors from Volkenrode which had not even been installed.

To cater for the new jet engine technologies the National Gas Turbine Establishment was created. Previously scattered over four sites, at Whetstone near Leicester, Pyestock near Farnborough, Lutterworth near Rugby, where the first Whittle engines were developed, and a London administrative office, the whole was eventually centred at Pyestock, where research now includes both aviation and non-aviation applications.

The scale of work required to build up the ground-based facilities for British post-war aeronautical research can perhaps be appreciated more fully from Appendix I, which lists the Ministry of Works Heavy Research Plant programme from 1945 to 1951 for the Bedford complex alone. This list is also taken from Mr Fletcher's lecture.

These vast undertakings in Bedfordshire and at Pyestock could not of

Photograph 9. 'Operation Surgeon', 1945–46. British military and civilian personnel outside the main entrance to the German Research Establishment at Göttingen. Left to right: Mr R. Goody, Mr Jack Hanson (Chief Scientist), W/Cdr H. Perring, AVM R. O. Jones (Deputy Controller R & D, Ministry of Aircraft Production), A/Cdr Hopkins (later killed on 'Operation Surgeon' flight), Mr G. W. Jones. (Note that civilians are in service uniform. This was a common practice in those uncertain days.)
(Picture kindly loaned by Mrs Lilian Hanson)

course become operational quickly. The burden of fundamental aircraft research in the immediate post-war years thus continued to lie on the shoulders of Farnborough, the National Physical Laboratory, and such facilities as were possessed by private firms and Universities. Their work constituted the real building bricks of aircraft design; much of it was painstaking measurement of an undramatic type, and as each item such as a wing section was tested so was a little more data placed in the hands of those who strove so desperately to create transonic aircraft. Perhaps some day a way will be found of affording the backroom workers some greater recognition of their ability and integrity.

61

The foregoing words merely summarize the British aviation scene immediately after World War II. It is hoped in the rest of this chapter not only to relate the facts but also to recapture the atmosphere of this period, which was in many ways similar to the 'Phoney War' phase in the latter half of 1939 – in both cases, forces were gathering and certain organizations existed. Nobody, however, quite knew how they were going to be used.

There is no doubt that despite the accumulation of considerable high-speed flight data from both home and overseas there was, in 1945, still a general feeling of extreme apprehension surrounding early attempts to exceed or even approach the speed of sound, and this stemmed not only from a basic human fear of the unknown but also from a suspicion that in this case the unknown might be even worse than expected. The imperfect understanding of the new aerodynamics existed in fact not from any want of effort in the early years but despite an extensive programme of experimental work, and the main problem was simply how to continue getting results. Scientific measurements were required under conditions never previously attempted and from this need for measurement came the first major cleavage of opinion in the research programme – should manned aircraft or pilotless models be used to obtain airborne data? This was something quite separate from any considerations of flight safety; if models could not make the measurements then it would be manned aircraft or nothing.

Now the procurement of model results depended on the transmission of radio signals from air to ground, and in the early days of transonic flight when none of the modern miniature, lightweight, transmitters existed, a model simply could not carry a worth-while quantity of radio equipment. The manned aircraft was therefore still an essential link in the chain but the cancellation of the Miles M52 in 1946 left Britain temporarily without a full-scale aircraft capable of supersonic speeds, so the model technique had to be tried. The de Havilland 108 was of course just commencing a test schedule but nothing was known of its handling qualities; it was not in any case part of the official government programme and as its main purpose was to obtain design information for a proposed civil airliner the inclusion of a supersonic flight research programme as such was not envisaged. Work had therefore been started by Vickers-Armstrongs Limited on the construction of twenty-five rocket-propelled flight models of a supersonic research aircraft based on the Miles M52 design. It was intended to investigate six different wing configurations, starting with the

Photograph 10. Vickers supersonic rocket-powered model aircraft during wind-tunnel tests.
(Royal Aircraft Establishment – Crown Copyright)

original upswept wing and then progress to various degrees of sweepback. One of the models is shown in Photograph 10, and each model was to be carried aloft to 36 000 ft beneath the belly of a Mosquito bomber. After release over an area near the Scilly Isles, an auto pilot was to level out the model, the rocket was then to fire and it was hoped that the flight path shown in Fig. 9 would result. In addition to any information transmitted from model to ground and from cameras in the carrier aircraft, a Meteor equipped with five cameras was provided for further photographing of the miniature aircraft in free flight. This was the plan – the reality was rather different. After the initial drop in 1947 had ended in failure, another model did, in October 1948, reach a speed of 930 miles/h in level flight ($1\cdot4 \times$ speed of sound), and it is fortunate that a picture sequence of this event was obtained from cine films (Photographs 11a–c). This shows (a) the model immediately after drop; (b) the firing of the rocket; and (c) the acceleration of the model to maximum speed. These pictures were

Photograph 11. *Vickers supersonic rocket-powered model in flight: (above) Just after release from beneath a Mosquito Bomber. (below) At moment of rocket firing. (opposite) After accelerating to supersonic speed.*
(Royal Aircraft Establishment – Crown Copyright)

obtained from an album of photographs belonging to Mr L. F. Nicholson, at one time Head of Supersonic Division, RAE Farnborough, and are so far the only airborne evidence known to exist of these experiments. (Mr Nicholson rose to the position of Vice-Controller of Aircraft, Ministry of Defence, before he retired in 1978.)

Measurements of speed, acceleration, and control angles were in fact successfully transmitted to the ground by telemetering and provided useful information on the transonic region, but the tests were not continued as each model cost £20 000 and a series of twenty-five would thus have consumed half a million pounds. When to this was added the operational cost of the aircraft and facilities, it amounted to the price of a full-sized manned aircraft in 1947 values. With the preparation time, hold-ups due to weather, aircraft unserviceability, short duration of flight, and difficulty of obtaining results also complicating the issue, an inflexible and uneconomic experiment was the inevitable result, and experience elsewhere had now reversed the early objection to the manned machine.

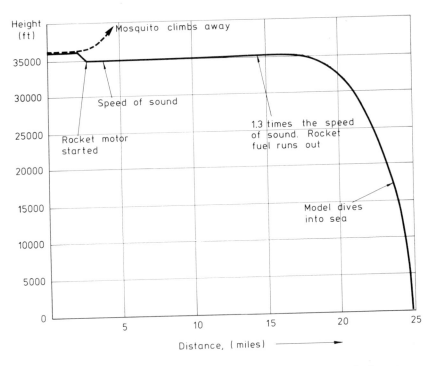

Figure 9. Vickers supersonic rocket-powered model aircraft. Flight path after release from Mosquito Bomber.

It should not, however, be thought that the Vickers' models lacked the careful preparation warranted by the expenditure. Photograph 12 shows the ground telemetering equipment installed to receive signals from the models – equipment whose modern equivalent could be contained in a handbag. The effort devoted to preparing the models themselves was also considerable and Mr C. Roberts, who was concerned with this work and who now works for British Aerospace at Chester, recently said:

> Dry air was required to spin up the model gyros as space on board was limited. Two compressors in tandem passed air through a 20 ft diameter fabric balloon containing many panels of absorbent material to take out oil and water. The air was then passed into another balloon, through a micro-filter, into an icebox and on to the aeroplane.

*Photograph 12. Telemetering equipment used to obtain results from Vickers
supersonic rocket-powered model.*
(Royal Aircraft Establishment – Crown Copyright)

Some idea of the internal complexity of each model can be seen in
Photograph 13 which shows the installed components.

An alternative method of launching auto pilot controlled models from
the ground was under active review in 1948 and the Fairey Aviation
Company commenced work on this technique. The intended models
possessed 60 degree swept wings and bore the same relationship to a likely
full-sized manned version, as did the Vickers models, to the Miles M52.
They were to have been propelled by Beta II rocket motors up to Mach
numbers of about 1·5. An auto pilot was being incorporated to maintain
level trimmed flight throughout the Mach number range but, as with the
Vickers' models, dependence on telemetry to obtain results was a main
area of difficulty. In the end the Fairey project was abandoned before even
one had been fired. Faireys were fully committed on guided weapon

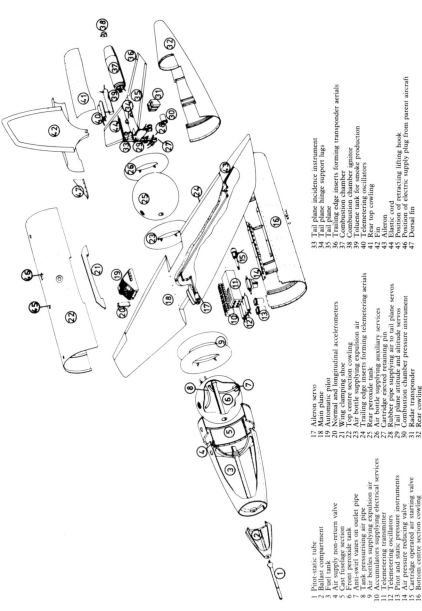

1 Pitot-static tube
2 Ballast compartment
3 Fuel tank
4 Air supply non-return valve
5 Cast fuselage section
6 Front peroxide tank
7 Anti-swirl vanes on outlet pipe
8 Tank pressurising air pipe
9 Air bottles supplying expulsion air
10 Accumulators supplying electrical services
11 Telemetering transmitter
12 Telemetering oscillators
13 Pitot and static pressure instruments
14 Air pressure reducing valve
15 Cartridge operated air starting valve
16 Bottom centre section cowling

17 Aileron servo
18 Main plane
19 Automatic pilot
20 Normal and longitudinal accelerometers
21 Wing clamping shoe
22 Top centre section cowling
23 Air bottle supplying expulsion air
24 Trailing edge inserts forming telemetering aerials
25 Rear peroxide tank
26 Air bottle supplying auxiliary services
27 Cartridge ejected retaining pin
28 Rubber pipe supplying air to tail plane servos
29 Tail plane attitude and altitude servos
30 Combustion chamber pressure instrument
31 Radar transponder
32 Rear cowling

33 Tail plane incidence instrument
34 Tail plane hinge support lugs
35 Tail plane
36 Trailing edge inserts forming transponder aerials
37 Combustion chamber
38 Combustion chamber ignitor
39 Toluene tank for smoke production
40 Telemetering oscillators
41 Rear top cowling
42 Fin
43 Aileron
44 Elastic cord
45 Position of retracting lifting hook
46 Position of electric supply plug from parent aircraft
47 Dorsal fin

Photograph 13. Vickers supersonic rocket-powered model aircraft. Layout of internal equipment.
(Royal Aircraft Establishment – Crown Copyright)

development although their ultimately famous delta winged Fairey Delta 2 was about to be conceived.

Of all the variations on the supersonic research theme one other must be mentioned in passing: it also concerns the Miles M52. After cancellation of the original project a proposal was made to fit an unmanned but full-size M52 with a rocket motor. In place of the pilot was to be installed an auto pilot and test instrumentation, the jet engine being replaced by rocket fuel tanks. It was intended to drop this machine from beneath a converted Lancaster bomber and, after a supersonic test flight, lower it by parachute into the sea, where it would have been supported by automatic flotation bags in the manner of present-day space capsules. This scheme was not pursued but typified the desperate gropings for the airborne evidence needed by wind-tunnel engineers to support or modify their conclusions.

As the limitations of unmanned miniature, or even full-size, aircraft for high Mach number research became increasingly apparent the potential of simpler experiments attracted attention. It was thought for instance that useful measurements might be made on small rocket-propelled models throughout all or part of their flight path. Such a technique was in contrast to previously envisaged auto pilot controlled model tests in which the collection of data was programmed for level flight. The idea possessed a big advantage in that the test methods measurement had, to some extent, been proved in the course of rocket missile trials. Disadvantages were that the flight time was short and information could only be obtained during an acceleration or deceleration. It was nevertheless a way of determining both aerodynamic and structural behaviour under conditions of speed and air density then unavailable in wind-tunnels.

By the end of 1950 sufficient progress had been made with rocket models for a widening field of work to be planned. Sponsored by RAE scientists the aims and policies were clearly expressed in an RAE Technical Memorandum dated October 1950. Two extracts from this document of particular significance are quoted here:

> The ground-launched rocket-boosted model technique is being developed by the R.A.E. as a main experimental method for aerodynamic investigation in the transonic region. Over the past 18 months the technique has been explored and we have developed its application to two problems, namely, the measurement of drag and control effectiveness. Lured on by a modicum of success in these simple cases, we are tempted to assault a more difficult problem, and one in which there is at present considerable interest, that of longitudinal stability.

. . . A basic tenet of our present creed is to begin experimentation with existing apparatus rather than to spend years developing the postulated ideal equipment before commencing the main aerodynamic research. We go for the simple experiment, accepting the answer it gives for what it is worth, and aim to improve the technique as we gain experience.

Thus was something learned of the new science.

Apart from their ability to make measurements beyond those available from theory and steady wind-tunnel conditions, rocket-propelled models also offered, at the time, almost the only means of investigating, in the absence of full-sized aircraft, the effects of atmospheric disturbances. These were becoming increasingly serious as speeds and heights increased, so the onward march of high-speed flight had to encompass every possible experimental technique.

What then of the manned experimental aircraft? None of these, apart from the M52, was expected to achieve supersonic speed even in a dive and, except for the short and determined effort of the de Havilland 108, none in their early years did. Although this situation was dictated primarily by economic circumstances, supersonic flight was still a military necessity, so what really mattered was how much effort could and should be devoted to transonic flight on the way. Should it be regarded merely as a pocket of resistance to be dealt with at a later date, or was it a major threat behind the lines needing immediate engagement?

The main problem was the transonic mixture of compressed and uncompressed flow mentioned briefly in Chapter 1. At subsonic speeds it was simple – there was no compression: at supersonic speeds it was all compression and these types of flow separately could be treated mathematically. But when the two were mixed at transonic speeds it was difficult to predict the location and effect of each type. This was particularly true during manoeuvres when quite small changes of speed, height, attitude, and control angle could cause not only a sudden change from one type of flow to another but rapidly fluctuating changes which produced severe buffeting.

The effects at first were several degrees worse than trying to control a car with loose steering in a gusting cross-wind, and as these confused patterns of behaviour were so difficult to calculate, the process of designing for transonic flight seemed at one time to be almost impossible.

One solution to the control problem, as indeed to any control problem, was to provide much more powerful and, if necessary, artificially powered

70

controls, but this did not remove the overall need to understand the airflow patterns and to identify the most troublesome elements therein.

There were nevertheless some, even in the ranks of the informed, who favoured an easy way out – provide enough engine power to accelerate quickly through the speed of sound, sit tight for a few seconds until the worst was over, and then fly serenely at supersonic speed. Such a philosophy was of course acceptable for experimental purposes, and indeed was applied, but no competent authority would approve an aeroplane for service, certainly not for commercial use, whose flight path was incapable of being predicted and controlled over a major part of its speed range. There was thus a clear commitment to tackle transonic flight sooner rather than later, and it was to this commitment that the glamour of the sound barrier became attached.

Up to the mid-1940s the outlook had not therefore been encouraging. In Britain as elsewhere there had been little immediate hope of reducing transonic drag substantially, certainly not with laminar flow or with flying wings, but the German work on swept wings had of course transformed the situation, and the ability of such wings to delay the onset of compressibility effects made available a new and highly worthwhile sector of operational speed. Jet propulsion could at last shake itself loose at least from one side of the sound barrier and commercial jet transport aircraft could be designed to expand the travelling facilities of our world.

The simple swept wing was in fact capable of much early refinement; for instance, when equipped with high lift devices for landing the result was a smaller basic wing with a reduction of cruising drag comparable to what might have resulted from laminar flow. There was, nevertheless, even more development potential in swept wing layouts and indeed the tailless swept wing continued to attract support for drag reduction, encouraged not only by the de Havilland 108 but also by the massive Northrop flying wing bombers in America. In Germany considerable attention had been paid to a particular tailless layout known as the delta wing (by comparison with the Greek letter Delta, written Δ), a concept capable of being mated with a conventional load-carrying fuselage, unlike the pure flying wing, which was in effect a wing, less fuselage. In recognition of the new situation the name of the Tailless Aircraft Committee was therefore changed to Swept Wing Committee on 12 March 1948, at its 36th and last meeting. It had been in existence for almost five years and had witnessed a momentous period of aviation history. One of its last acts, unfortunately, was to record the death of Squadron Leader Robert Kronfeld, at the time a test pilot with General Aircraft Limited and who had just been killed testing a tailless glider.

But wings were not the only problem. As far as the fuselage was concerned this assembly did not seem to offer much scope for contributing in any large measure to the new demands of high Mach number flight. Its cross-sectional area was dictated by the need to accommodate crew, equipment, and possibly engines, and the slimness needed to avoid large contour changes was not always easy to achieve. The most unpredictable airflows were present at the junctions of major components such as fuselage, wing, and tail, so that trial and error methods were often the quickest means of resolving optimum shapes. Early research into such junctions did, however, produce designs which smoothed the passage of the air and gave considerable drag reductions, although this sometimes resulted in shapes quite at variance with the traditional idea of stream-lining, the main purpose being to reduce the speed of the air at local points and prevent the formation of shock waves. This did, however, raise problems of manufacture.

In the days when high Mach number flight was in its infancy the aerodynamic causes of undesirable handling effects could often be attributed to sources other than the wing or main fuselage. Engine nacelles, cockpit canopies, and external stores influenced overall airflow patterns to a marked degree and this was particularly so at speeds around the critical Mach number. Due to lack of experience in design and diagnosis, however, it was some time before solutions to handling deficiencies in compressible flow conditions could be predicted with certainty and, even when found, sometimes produced serious deteriorations in aircraft performance.

All this was of course to be considered by the new Swept Wing Committee, whose first meeting was held on Friday, 21 May 1948, in Thames House, London, the Chair being taken by Mr H. M. Garner (later Sir Harry Garner), then Principal Director of Scientific Research – Air [PDSR(A)] in the Ministry of Supply.

It was emphasized that whereas the Tailless Aircraft Committee had concerned itself mostly with low-speed matters and then only on tailless aircraft, the Swept Wing Committee would focus more on high-speed work on all types of aircraft, tailed or tailless. The terms of reference were finally stated to be:

To advise PDSR(A) on the practical aspects of the flight and wind tunnel research programme of swept wings.

To discuss the results of theoretical and practical work at firms and Establishments and to exchange information on problems of mutual interest.

A progress summary of the major projects was given and the situation was as follows:

TAILLESS GLIDERS

General Aircraft Limited

Replacement pilot for Squadron Leader Kronfeld awaited. More tests to take place soon.

Armstrong-Whitworth

No work. No glider tug available.

POWERED AIRCRAFT

Armstrong-Whitworth

AW.52. Had flown a total of nine and a half hours.

de Havilland

DH.108 Swallow.

Low-speed aircraft: flying continuing.

High-speed aircraft: had flown up to 0·9 Mach and to airspeed of 643 miles/h.

Boulton Paul

Delta E27/46.

First aircraft two-thirds complete.

Second aircraft to be modified for moving wing tips.

Handley-Page Aircraft Limited

Bomber B35/46. Still in design phase.

Experimental aircraft E6/48. A scale model of a proposed bomber stated to have a crescent planform wing fitted to a Supermarine Attacker fuselage.

A. V. Roe Limited

Bomber B35/46. No flight date given.

Experimental aircraft E15/48 and E16/48. Scale models of bomber. No flight dates given.

Hawker Aircraft

Experimental fighter E38/46 nearly finished and expected to fly in August 1948. This aircraft was stated to be a development of the straight winged N7/46 with a 35 degree swept wing and a straight tail with a possible delta-tailed alternative.

Supermarine Aviation

Experimental fighter E41/46 nearly complete and expected to fly in about two months. High-speed tunnel tests in progress.

Bristol Aircraft

Experimental aircraft E8/47. A modified design of a scale model bomber with 45 degree wing sweep and an all moving tailplane.

Fairey Aviation

Experimental aircraft E10/47 (and half-scale pilotless models). To be flown initially as conventional aircraft but later with rockets to give near vertical take-off. Nene Jet engine to be fitted. Half-scale models to be rocket powered and hoped to fly first to obtain preliminary flight information.

Gloster Aircraft Limited

Little information available. Stated to be delta wing with all moving delta tailplane.

As far as practical flying experience went it can thus be seen that significant progress had been made only with the de Havilland 108, and even then at Mach numbers lower than the Spitfire.

We have talked so far of shapes, thrust, and drag but we must now say more about controls, and by this we mean the external control surfaces such as elevators, ailerons, rudders, as well as their means of operation. Whatever may have been misunderstood originally about compressible flow, one need was clearly established in the minds of scientists and pilots alike, and this was to improve flying controls; controls to enable still

74

higher speeds to be achieved for research purposes and controls sufficient to allow operational pilots the benefit of safe and pleasant flight throughout the new-found ranges of speed and height. For some years, even before the first excursions near the speed of sound, the matter of aircraft control had, however, been throwing up new problems; as speeds had increased so had the forces needed to move the main flying control surfaces. To some extent reductions of control force had been achieved by careful balancing both of the surfaces themselves and their operating mechanisms, but anything finely balanced can be moved by the slightest disturbance and aircraft controls were no exception. Small changes of contour could upset the trimming and manoeuvring power of all controls, or a wrongly calculated balance could cause not only the control surfaces but also the main lifting surfaces to vibrate uncontrollably, sometimes to destruction. We have already mentioned in Chapter 1 the phenomena of aeroelasticity in general, and flutter in particular, the latter being one name for the vibrations just described, but these tended to become much more worrying when associated first with the wildly fluctuating air loads of the transonic region and later with the massive loads of supersonic flight whether in conjunction with heating effects or not. In fact, the finely balanced flying control became in many cases a menace near the speed of sound, a situation which called increasingly for some form of more rigid, power-operated, system.

Another important cleavage of opinion therefore arose and was centred around the extent to which powered controls should replace or supplement pilot effort. The use of mechanical or electrical devices to control other forms of transport vehicle – for example, the power-operated rudders of large ships – had been an established practice for many years, and although reliability in such systems was desirable, any failure was, at the worst, inconvenient. With aircraft, on the other hand, the failure of a powered-control system could lead to disaster, so, in this case, reliable operation meant continuous operation and nothing less. The matter was of great importance and on 27 August 1947 a meeting was held at the RAE Farnborough to discuss the various features involved. Under the Chairmanship of Mr W. G. A. Perring, then Director of the Establishment, about 200 people representing the industry and research units attended to hear papers presented by scientists, engineers, and pilots intimately concerned with the subject. Out of the extensive discussion which followed the meeting, one item in particular tantalized those responsible for future development, namely, the need for providing the pilot with emergency manual control in the event of power control failure. There were three possibilities, the first being to rely entirely on duplicated powered controls, the second to have powered controls with a manual reversion system for use only in the event of power failure, and the third being merely a manual system with power boosting, the manual element being the main system and working at all times. In his summing up of the meeting Mr Perring expressed the following opinions in relation to the manual control controversy:

> Now let me come to the points upon which there is still a fair measure, if not of disagreement, then of honest doubt. There is the question of the need for manual reversion. I must say in listening to the discussion I find it very difficult to make up my own mind on the issue. There appeared to be some who while arguing for manual reversion in one breath, were arguing against it in the next. My own feeling about the whole business is that we must put reliability first, and by ensuring ourselves of 100 per cent reliability, we should then be able to face systems in which manual reversion is eliminated. That, at least, should be our target.

Considerable development was needed before the art of designing powered flying controls reached the stage where reversion to manual means in emergency could be dispensed with entirely. Of the early jet aircraft fitted with powered controls some did in fact incorporate a manual reversion system but this was omitted in later designs when the reliability necessary for both military and civil aircraft requirements had been achieved. From that moment the full potential of jet power lay open to designers although the satisfactory movement of a control by mechanical or electric motors did not necessarily mean that the aircraft would respond in a desired fashion. That was an aerodynamic problem and a group of RAE test pilots in contributing to a document entitled 'Notes on the Flying Qualities of High Speed Designs as seen by Test Pilots' expressed the following view:

> It is the general opinion of the R.A.E. Test Pilots that the most important requirement in high speed research aircraft is the ability to retain control at all times. If this can be assured, and there seems to be no reason why it cannot be, then pilots will be able to take the aircraft to much higher Mach numbers than heretofore, confident in their ability to retain control of the aeroplane. In this way a great deal of valuable data may be obtained comparatively quickly.

These words were written in 1950 and it was perhaps unfortunate that in those days little could be assured where control in the transonic regions was concerned and some lives were to be lost in proving the point. What were the primary difficulties? Of major concern was the longitudinal control which determines the manner in which an aircraft climbs or dives – particularly the latter. For aircraft possessing a tailplane it became apparent at an early stage that the vertical position of this component in relation to the wing was critical for minimizing and counteracting the trim and manoeuvrability changes due to Mach number, the reason being that as Mach number changed so did the angle at which the air was deflected downwards from the wing to the tail. So once more the question of tailless aircraft arose, not this time for drag reduction, but to escape from the critical requirement of tail position. The pure flying wing was not, as it happened, any more beneficial in this respect than it was for high speed, the short leverage of the trailing edge controls introducing more problems than it solved, but the delta variant was a different matter. This layout being very highly swept did give a fairly large control leverage and over the years it has been adopted on aircraft both large and small with considerable success. The delta structure also had the advantage of rigidity being concentrated around the centre of gravity and this feature helped to maintain the control rigidity needed both for transonic and supersonic flight.

However, with the onset of compressible flow, severe control problems other than longitudinal arose. Sudden disturbances in the rolling and directional senses were experienced and these did not always respond to the most powerful aileron and rudder applications – of if they did respond, the response could be wild and unexpected. Severe rolling motions caused by partial wing stalling frequently limited the speed of an aircraft before the structural strength limit was even reached. But such efforts were not always precisely repeatable and this made a remedy difficult to determine.

Small wonder that the expression 'sound barrier' came to describe an unprecedented situation in which the motion of an aircraft in every direction could be complicated by airflow changes of tremendous proportions. For many years aircraft design had been by experimental and intuitive methods but the problems involved in raising speeds beyond that of sound finally transported the design process into the realms of scientific research. The dawn of aviation had then given way to the day, but the day had, rather unkindly, become somewhat foggy.

We shall now focus our attention on the immediate post-World War II British research aircraft on which so many hopes were centred, their basic requirements being clearly expressed as follows by two RAE scientists, Mr S. B. Gates and Mr Handel Davies, in an RAE Technical Memorandum of April 1950:

Our object is to develop jet aircraft of fixed geometrical form to cruise at high altitude and high speed. The immediate aim is to postpone the drag rise as far as possible and cruise just short of it; the ultimate to fly straight through to a supersonic (i.e., shock free) cruising speed. Wherever in this scheme the cruising speed is placed, the transonic region, where shock waves induce abrupt changes in lift distribution, lies like a patch of very rough water across the field of research. This region can be postponed in the scale of M but it cannot ultimately be evaded; it is probable that it can never be smoothed out; we have yet to chart its currents; and at the moment we must give the pilots enough control to navigate chartless through them.

Even before the end of the war in 1945, two new experimental jet aircraft were in fact under construction, the Supermarine E10/44, a single-seat fighter, and the Armstrong-Whitworth AW.52, a slightly swept flying wing for research into civil transport applications. The E10/44 was designed to take advantage of the new high-thrust Rolls-Royce Nene engine. It possessed a truly bullet-shaped fuselage, an unswept nominally laminar flow wing, and first flew on 27 July 1946. The wing was not in fact entirely new. It had originally been developed for a late Mark of Spitfire but this became so different from earlier versions that a new name – Spiteful – was allocated (see Photograph 14). A Naval variant called Seafang also flew. Both were capable of almost 500 miles/h but neither went into service, having been ousted by the jets. Being the successor to Supermarine's famous Spitfire, the E10/44 was naturally assured of a popular following. Its speed, however, was not sufficiently greater than the later Meteors to be of advantage to the Royal Air Force, but the Royal Navy became interested and with the name of Attacker it saw service on both shore bases and on aircraft carriers. In passing it may be noted that in 1948 an Attacker prototype flown by the late M. J. Lithgow gained the 100 km closed-circuit speed record at 546·9 miles/h.

Following the Attacker, the Armstrong-Whitworth AW.52 (Photograph 15), a most graceful creation, first flew on 13 November 1947, and although not intended for quantity production it nevertheless conformed to every schoolboy's idea of a futuristic ship of the air. It was designed as a small-scale model of a six-jet flying wing airliner but only two AW.52s were built, one with two Rolls-Royce Nene engines and the other with two Rolls-Royce Derwents. The Nene-powered version flew first, piloted by

Photograph 14. Supermarine 'Spiteful' Fighter with laminar flow wing. Seen here with tail hook for deck landing. Naval version known as 'Seafang'.
(Supermarine–Vickers Limited)

Photograph 15. Armstrong-Whitworth AW.52 Flying Wing.
(British Aerospace)

the firm's experimental test pilot, Squadron Leader E. G. Franklin. It was a fairly large aircraft with a wing span of 90 ft and an all-up weight of about 33 000 lb, and something had already been learned of its handling characteristics on a 53-ft-span scale model manned glider first flown in March 1945. Despite the fact that natural laminar flow had not proved practically possible an attempt had, however, been made on the AW.52 to induce this condition for use at low speeds, the main emphasis being to prevent wing tip stalling and thus to lower the landing speed. To do this a boundary layer suction system had been incorporated in which the layer of air immediately next to the upper wing skin was sucked away through narrow slots to prevent flow breakaway, the suction being provided from the enormous air flow through the jet engines. This is another advantage of jet propulsion and the principle is sound, but there are practical disadvantages. Large lengths of internal piping are required and these, apart from being expensive, take up valuable space inside the structure. The suction slots are, moreover, narrow and can be clogged by small particles or ice. There is in addition some loss of power due to air being taken from the engines. An alternative system involves blowing a supply of air over the wing surfaces, again taken from the engine supply, and whilst military aircraft have made use of the system it has not been applied commercially. Improved jet engine performance and the recent interest in short take-off and landing for transport aircraft have, however, promoted a revival of interest in airflow control systems after a long period in which high landing speeds at large airfields have had to be accepted.

The AW.52 was a remarkable structural achievement. A wing contour accuracy of one two-thousandth of an inch was claimed in the effort to assist laminar flow but an onset of uncontrollable pitching motion eventually caused the loss of the first Nene engined version on 30 May 1949. The pilot at the time was J. Lancaster who saved his life using an ejector seat, the first person outside America to do so.

Some details of this accident were presented to the 16th meeting of the Swept Wing Committee on 15 September 1950, when it was said:

Whilst descending from 10,000 feet at 320 knots turbulent air was encountered at 5,000 feet. This started a longitudinal oscillation of about two cycles per second. The pilot braced the control column but the oscillation, instead of damping out as on previous occasions continued to increase. . . . As the oscillations continued to increase the pilot throttled back and tried easing back the stick, but this had no effect. The oscillations finally became so violent that the pilot used the ejection seat for fear that he would become unconscious. The total time from commencement of the oscillation to the time the pilot left the aircraft was about 15 secs.

Two points of particular interest arise from this account, the first being the persistence of the oscillation after action had been taken to reduce speed, a very dangerous condition, leaving the pilot with little scope for further remedial action. The second point is the very short time available for action to be taken. In this case the pilot was forced to abandon the aircraft after only 15 s, a pattern to be repeated many times in the ensuing years, sometimes with the loss also of the pilot.

So the second AW.52 continued the flying programme but the type marked the end of serious work on flying wings in Britain, for it was becoming clear that conventional layouts with separate load-carrying fuselages, with swept wings or otherwise, lent themselves more readily to future change or growth. A fuselage could easily be lengthened to carry, say, more passengers without seriously affecting the lifting efficiency of the wing or moving its internal equipment. With a flying wing, on the other hand, the job was much more difficult. Everything was carried within the wing and a rearrangement of one thing meant moving another. The alternative was to increase the size of the wing but as this could mean an almost complete aerodynamic redesign, to say nothing of the structure, a prohibitive cost was a distinct possibility.

With both laminar flow and flying wings being non-starters, what might be called Britain's twilight years of the sound barrier thus ended with the AW.52 design. So with swept wings being clearly in the ascendancy it may seem appropriate at this stage to go back momentarily to 1945 and see what view of the immediate future was then being taken by those great practitioners of supersonic experiment, the Germans. From the American Combined Intelligence Objectives sub-committee (G2 Division SHAEF) report on the interrogation of some German scientists, the views of the late Dr Alexander Lippisch, a firm believer in delta wings, were recorded as follows:

Tail-less and Tailed Aeroplanes
Although the use of sweepback was, in general, prevalent throughout the German airplane designing brotherhood, there was some resistance to its full use in making the airplane tail-less . . . a flying wing. Both Messerschmitt and Focke-Wulf were working on airplanes with swept back wings and swept back tails. Both had a similar reason; they felt that for flight at high Mach number

81

the tail-less airplane was unsatisfactory because it lacked sufficient control and damping in the pitching plane to counteract pitching oscillations. It should be noted that they are specifically referring to the region just beyond Mcr* where violent changes in trim occur.

Dr. Lippisch takes an opposite view. He believes that no tailed airplane has yet stopped the violent instability that occurs above Mcr and further states that the flow at the tail for these Mach numbers is so independent and so impossible to calculate that no tail ever could be *designed* to give the desired controllability. Also he believes that the most logical means of controlling the sudden changes in pitching moment is to control the wing airfoil shape as is done with the tail-less airplane.

But probably of most importance is Lippisch's statement that the unstable region above Mcr should not be flown through in level flight but rather in a zero lift dive (or climb) so that there need not be any moment change (if a symmetrical airfoil is used).

The tailed versus tailless controversy raged for some years, but, whilst contrary to the fears of Dr Lippisch (and he was not alone in these fears), it was eventually possible to design a tail giving full and predictable control in the transonic region, the tailless aeroplane in delta winged form became a separate and outstanding success story. His suggestion to dive or climb through the worst of the sound barrier can of course be contrasted with the alternative suggestion already mentioned of accelerating through quickly in level flight. Both ideas were a temporary expedient and both were of use in experimental work, but neither were of operational value.

(NOTE: In strict order we should now describe the de Havilland 108 tailless swept wing research aircraft, but as this was the first British machine to exceed $M = 1$ and is of such individual interest, the whole of Chapter 4 has been devoted to its story. We continue therefore further into the swept wing era.)

By 1948 the initial excitement over jet propulsion had begun to subside and British aircraft development was looking a little outdated compared with progress overseas. It was thus heartening when, towards the end of 1948, the two aircraft whose purpose was to investigate swept wing behaviour made their maiden flights. Their appearance and ancestry satisfied the most fastidious connoisseurs. The machines in question were the Hawker 1052 (first flew 19 November 1948 – Photograph 16a), and the Supermarine 510 (first flew 29 December 1948 – Photograph 16b), whose

---

* Author's reminder: Mcr is the Mach number at which compressibility effects are first detected.

82

*Photograph 16a. Hawker P.1052 swept wing research aircraft seen here with
original unswept tailplane.*
(British Aerospace)

*Photograph 16b. Supermarine Type 510. The first British jet-propelled aircraft with
sweepback on both wing and tail surfaces.*
(Supermarine–Vickers Limited)

forebears, the Hurricane and Spitfire, respectively, had fought and won the Battle of Britain. Both the 1052 and the 510 had Rolls-Royce Nene engines and were conversions of existing straight winged aircraft, the Hawker 1040 and Supermarine Attacker. The 1052 was a Hawker P1040 fuselage with a 35 degree swept wing, the original unswept tail surfaces being retained. The Supermarine 510, on the other hand, was an Attacker fuselage with not only a 40 degree swept wing but also with swept back tail surfaces, this being Britain's first all swept aeroplane of separate wing and tail layout.

It was soon apparent, as the Germans had found, that sweep back could make greater Mach numbers and speeds possible. The more violent high Mach number effects, however, whilst certainly delayed by sweepback, were not diminished. It was thus important that these two aircraft should obtain information not only on pure aerodynamic features but also on the likely operational limitations of swept wing fighters. British versions of these were only then being specified, less still designed, nearly two years after the Americans had produced their F86 Sabre and de Havilland had first flown the DH.108. So there was little time to lose but had such fighters been available in 1948 it is doubtful if, with their non-supersonic performance and limited fighting equipment, they could have done much to defend the British Isles against a determined nuclear attack. Eventually a 1052 was fitted with a variable incidence swept tailplane (Photograph 17a) and flight trials with this equipment continued until a forced landing in late 1953 brought its life to a premature end.

Two 1052s were built and the second was eventually converted to the type 1081 with all swept surfaces and a single jet pipe in the tail (Photograph 17b). This latter replaced the earlier split jet pipes on either side of the fuselage and was meant to permit the installation of reheat. The Australian Government expressed some interest in the 1081 as a fighter but did not finally make a purchase. In the end the 1081 crashed, killing the Chief Test Pilot of Hawker Aircraft Limited, Trevor Wade, in circumstances never fully explained.

Two Supermarine 510s were likewise built in the firm's experimental hangar at Hursley Park near Winchester. The first (Serial No. VV106) had a tailwheel undercarriage, and early in the flight programme achieved Mach numbers around 0·95. This was a step in the right direction and in 1950 it was assessed by pilots from both Boscombe Down and RAE Farnborough.

Photograph 17a. Hawker P.1052 as later fitted with a swept back tailplane. This aircraft is shown here at the Royal Air Force Museum at Cosford where it is now preserved.
(Royal Air Force Museum, Cosford)

Photograph 17b. Hawker P.1081. Converted from 1052 by fitting new rear fuselage with jet pipe in tail and all swept tail surfaces. The painted forward portion of the fuselage and the wing are the original 1052 components.
(British Aerospace)

In the autumn of 1950 VV106 was extensively instrumented for trials on an aircraft carrier, and when it finally went to sea in November 1950 it made the first landing by any swept wing aircraft on an aircraft carrier (Photograph 18), a noteworthy feat at a time when much still remained to be learned about low-speed handling with swept wings. The most exciting moment of these trials came, however, on a take-off. Rocket packs for extra take-off thrust were mounted on each side of the fuselage and on the last take-off the rockets on one side failed to give full thrust. The aircraft swung rapidly towards the side of the deck, a wing tip hit the top of a gun turret and the pilot, Lt-Cdr D. G. Parker (later Rear-Admiral Parker) only just managed to maintain control and take-off.

The second Type 510, VV119, was flown with a tailwheel for only a short period before being converted to a nosewheel layout (Photograph 19), after which it received the new type number 535. This was a most fateful conversion which initiated a turbulent episode in the history of Super-marines, but for the moment it can be said that when VV106 made its first public appearance at the Farnborough Show in 1949 it was the centre of attraction and its high-speed runs will always be remembered by those present.

So Britain now had three swept wing experimental aeroplanes including the de Havilland 108, and although they yielded much useful data, they did not in the eyes of the general public even begin to chase the Americans up the Mach number ladder. It was a frustrating situation needing much patience to understand. In 1944 a Spitfire had achieved a Mach number of over 0·9 with a piston engine and simple manual controls which were surprisingly trouble-free. Yet, in 1950, despite the presence of jet engines and the development of new aerodynamic shapes, only the DH.108 had made much progress in terms of Mach number – and basically manual controls were still used although with small degrees of power boosting. Suitable comment was made in test reports and in an RAE Technical Memorandum, dated November 1950, when the Hawker 1052 and Supermarine 510 were compared with earlier straight winged aircraft.

It would appear from the tests on these two aircraft that although it is possible for the trim change problem to be delayed by sweepback to a higher Mach number, basically it is no easier than a straight winged aircraft. . . . The position is complicated further by a possible reduction in control effectiveness at Mach numbers above 0·9 . . . it is sufficient here to stress the point that until we understand much more about these transonic trim changes and can reduce

Photograph 18. Supermarine Type 510, VV106, shown here, performing the first landings by a swept wing jet fighter on an aircraft carrier, HMS Illustrious, November 1950. The small box under the fuselage carried cameras to photograph the undercarriage legs.
(Fleet Air Arm Museum, Yeovilton)

them by skilful design, we must provide the pilot with effective controls and sufficient power to use them. This implies fitting irreversible power operated controls . . . and an all moving tail to cope with what might otherwise be large stick movements.

Again in a Technical Memorandum from which we have already quoted, the need for power controls was emphasized in no uncertain terms.

It is notable that the revolution in planform has not, to date, brought a revolution in the control system. . . . While the transonic trim changes remain largely unpredictable, the obviously correct policy is to give the pilot large control surfaces and power to move them quickly enough to counter unstable movements. For example, the whole tail should be moveable, whether or not an elevator is fitted. From this point of view the transonic stability problem remains acute . . . large and ample control is a first line of defence. . . .

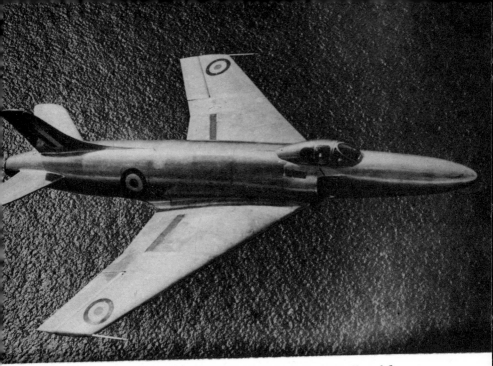

Photograph 19. Supermarine Type 535, VV119. Originally built and flown as a Type 510. Given type number 535 after lengthening of nose and fitting of nosewheel-type undercarriage. Wing centre section area increased by increasing sweep of leading edge and reducing sweep of trailing edge. This aircraft featured in the film
Sound Barrier.
(Supermarine–Vickers Limited)

Three years after their first flights both the 1052 and the 510 had played a large part in smoothing the way for the Hunter and Swift fighters, respectively, but even these later aircraft initially lacked powered controls.

In the meanwhile, a programme of work had started on delta wings which were a very unknown quantity even though the Germans had devoted some time to their study. Today the delta layout is commonplace, the latest variants being Concorde and the Space Shuttle, and it might be said that British delta aircraft, both large and small, have been among the most successful in the world. But in 1949, when even a simple swept wing was still a much-feared device, the delta seemed a truly futuristic concept, and it might be worth noting that despite the possession of some of the most advanced wind-tunnel facilities, the first American attempt at a supersonic delta wing fighter, the F102, was initially a disaster, which only their immense production capacity managed finally to retrieve, although the trouble lay not so much with the wing itself as with the high drag of the wing/fuselage junction.

Despite the advantages offered by the delta, however, with greater elevator control leverage and greater structural rigidity than with the simple flying wing, concern was still expressed over the fitting of landing flaps to the wing trailing edge and the consequent trim changes which might require a separate tailplane to counteract. The alternative was to land at such high angles of incidence that the pilot's view of the runway might be impaired, but it was feared that a loss of directional stability might then occur due to the blanking of the fin by the wing. Both these fears were in fact allayed, but generally the delta problem at first looked formidable, not only because it was something new but because the newness was associated with the equally new environment of transonic and supersonic flight. Three groups of deltas were planned to undertake manned experimental flying; all were small and single engined and the first, built by Avro, was known as the Type 707 (Photograph 20). Intended primarily to provide information for the design of a big delta winged bomber (the Vulcan), there were four versions of this aircraft, the 707, 707A, 707B, and 707C, the last of these being a side-by-side two-seater. Each was powered by a Rolls-Royce Derwent engine and when the first (VX784) made a maiden flight on 4 September 1949, this was also the first-ever flight of a British delta. The pilot on this occasion was Mr S. E. Esler, who was unfortunately killed a few weeks later when this aircraft crashed, on 30 September, near Blackbushe airport.

Boulton Paul Aircraft Limited were next to enter the delta programme when their single-seat P111 first flew in October 1950. They subsequently produced two variants of this, the P111A and P120. All were powered by a Rolls-Royce Nene engine thus having about 40 per cent more thrust than the Avro 707 series.

Fairey Aviation Limited were the third of the early delta trio, when their diminutive FD1 first flew on 10 March 1951. Powered like the Avro 707 by a Rolls-Royce Derwent engine, this aircraft was not itself of major importance but its successor, the Fairey Delta 2, most certainly was, as Chapter 6 relates.

How did these deltas contribute to the overall programme?

The Avro aircraft investigated a wide range of speed and Mach number

Photograph 20. The family of Avro 707 experimental delta aircraft shown here in 1953 in company with the two prototype Vulcan Bombers VX770 and VX777 to the development of which they contributed.
(British Aerospace)

nearly up to the speed of sound. They particularly made a contribution to the knowledge of low-speed handling. For the most part they displayed none of the frightening effects which had been feared and in many reports of their behaviour it is difficult to find the sort of severe criticisms which were often levelled at early swept wings. Some basic aerodynamic modifications found necessary for the Vulcan were investigated with the 707 family. Typical of these were changes to the wing leading edges, to improve performance, and various engine air intake designs.

Boulton Paul's programme was Britain's main delta research effort and was thus not aimed at promoting a specific project. Speeds up to, but not beyond, the speed of sound were required. The first aircraft, the P111 (Photograph 21a), had completed about fifty hours flying, all by Ministry test pilots, when a wheels up forced landing had to be made at Boscombe Down early in 1952. The aircraft was returned to the makers for repair and the fitting of an advanced flying control system with the then novelty of variable gearing between the control column and the control surfaces. This enabled the pilot to select the most suitable sensitivity for a particular flight condition and followed the discovery that, at high speeds, the controls were far too sensitive for accurate test work, control sensitivity having become a general problem caused by the wider speed, height, and Mach number ranges made possible by jet propulsion. With the new controls the P111 was known as the P111A.

The idea for the variable gear control system belonged to the late 'Jock' Elliot, once a Royal Navy officer and a graduate of No. 7 ETPS course. It was proposed at a meeting at Boulton Paul, attended by the firm's Chief Engineer, the late J. D. North, and by their Chief Test Pilot, A. E. (Ben) Gunn (at present Airport Manager at Shoreham). Elliot was, at that time,

Photograph 21a. Boulton Paul P111 experimental delta aircraft. The black, pointed tips of the wings and fin could be removed to investigate the effect on handling.
(Boulton Paul)

a test pilot in the Aerodynamics Flight Section at the RAE Farnborough, the Head of which was Mr Handel Davies, who said:

> Elliot was an outstanding man. When others were groping in the dark, Elliot put his finger on the solution.

It was perhaps fortunate, however, that J. D. North had always been interested in control theory and in the 1930s had brought Boulton Paul into the field of aircraft power-operated gun turrets. These made a great contribution to Royal Air Force successes from 1939 to 1945 and after the war North continued his research into control design. In consequence, Boulton Paul became a major contractor for the powered flying controls so necessary for high Mach number flight and they were thus well placed to develop this aspect of their own delta aeroplane. It is a pity that Boulton Paul did not continue in the front rank of aeroplane constructors, as their early, and substantial, contribution to supersonic flight tends to become overshadowed in consequence.

The later Boulton Paul delta, the P120 (Photograph 21b), gave great promise but had a chequered career. It differed from the P111 in having a small tailplane for trimming. The first flight was hardly encouraging and in describing it to the author, Mr Gunn, who flew the machine, said:

> The P120 made an eventful first flight on 6th August, 1952, at Boscombe Down. The nose wheel shed its tread on take-off due to excessive speed: the aircraft refusing to get airborne until a speed of 185 knots had been reached. At unstick the whole of Boscombe Down's massive runway had been used up and it was later found that the tail trimmer setting for take-off had been miscalculated.

He landed safely.

Following this embarrassment a good but short programme of flying was undertaken. The tailplane gave an improvement in longitudinal stability and confidence was being gained when, on 29 August 1952, with 'Ben' Gunn again at the controls, an occurrence of control flutter forced him to eject over Salisbury Plain and the aircraft was lost. In some ways this was a fortunate accident. The P120 was due to appear the following week at the Farnborough Show. Had it survived and flown on the Monday it might well have crashed, possibly into the crowd. At the end of the same week on the Saturday, John Derry crashed in the de Havilland 110, killing himself, his observer, Tony Richards, and twenty-eight spectators. A double tragedy in one week may thus have been narrowly avoided.

Photograph 21b. Boulton Paul P120. Developed from the P111 it was fitted with horizontal tail surfaces.
(Boulton Paul)

Following the P120 crash, the P111A, with the variable control gearing, was flown by the firm at Boscombe Down between 2 July 1953 and 14 January 1954. After that the official research programme continued with Ministry test pilots, the last flight being made at the RAE Bedford on 20 June 1958. Mach numbers up to 0·98 were achieved (i.e., up to the speed of sound) as specified. In general no serious problems were encountered and good agreement was obtained between full-scale and wind-tunnel tests. In particular, it was stated that the Boulton Paul powered flying controls had proved extremely reliable under every condition of test, a very satisfactory result in this most important of all contributions to supersonic flight.

Finally, the name of Fairey Aviation entered the delta scene and their FD1 of only 19 ft 6 in wing span (Photograph 22) had been preceded by extensive wind-tunnel testing as well as the flying of a radio-controlled

Photograph 22. Fairey FD1. Experimental delta aircraft. Originally proposed for vertical take off with rockets but finally flown in conventional manner with undercarriage.
(Fairey Aviation Limited)

model. The FD1 was originally conceived to be launched almost vertically from a short ramp. Model tests for this purpose had been conducted in Cardigan Bay starting in May 1949, and it was eventually intended to conduct full-scale trials. The outcome of the FD1 was to be a rapid climbing interceptor fighter. In the end it was fitted with an undercarriage and after a comparatively short life was completely overshadowed by its illustrious successor, the FD2. The FD2 design had progressed some way when the FD1 first flew and it took over where the Boulton Paul deltas left off, at the speed of sound, which it soon left far behind.

To complete the story of post-1945 new wing shapes we should mention the Handley-Page HP.88. This was a crescent winged research aircraft for supporting the Victor bomber programme in the same way that Avro's 707 helped the Vulcan. The HP.88 was simply a Supermarine 510 (i.e. modified Attacker) fuselage fitted with a crescent wing and tailplane (Photographs 23a and b). The conversion work was undertaken by

Photographs 23a and b. Handley-Page 88 experimental aircraft. Built to support the Victor Bomber programme, this machine was a Supermarine Type 510 fuselage fitted with a crescent wing of the planform intended for the Victor.
(British Aerospace)

Blackburn and General Aircraft Limited at Brough and the first flight was made on 1 May 1951 from the RAF wartime emergency airfield at Carnaby, near Bridlington, Yorkshire. Only two months later, however, the aircraft crashed. When being flown by Douglas Broomfield, the Deputy Chief Test Pilot of Handley-Page Limited, the HP.88 was approaching Stansted airfield in Essex when at 200 ft it was seen to pull up into a short climb. It then broke up, killing the pilot, wing flutter being diagnosed as the cause of the accident. Broomfield was the thirty-second test pilot to be killed in Britain in the six years following the end of the war.

This grim total in some way justified the initial concern for pilots of supersonic aircraft. The value of saving a pilot, particularly a test pilot, was not just a question of ensuring the continuing use of his experience. It was all important to establish the cause of any accident and nothing could do this better than the report of a surviving pilot. British work on ejector seats started in 1944 and from the earliest days played a leading role in equipping both home-produced and foreign aircraft. Preliminary tests were made with ground rigs and dummies ejected from an experimental Boulton Paul Defiant fighter, the first live ejection taking place on 24 July 1946, when Mr Bernard Lynch, of the Martin Baker Aircraft Company Limited, ejected from a Meteor during a test at 8000 ft and 320 miles/h. Lynch's pioneering work made one of the greatest individual contributions to flight safety since parachutes were developed. Although not directly part of a high-speed flight programme it nevertheless ensured that certain tests could be conducted with confidence which otherwise might not have been possible.

On looking back, therefore, British post-war transonic research might be seen to deserve more praise than it often receives. Progress may sometimes have seemed slow but it was thorough and, in consequence, that much more valuable.

4

THE EARLY BIRD

On 27 July 1945, a member of the de Havilland Aircraft Company's aerodynamics staff was preparing to go on leave. He left a note for a colleague attached to some calculations which comprised the previous week's activities. The first few lines of the note (which still exists in the de Havilland archives) read as follows:

> There has been great flapping and scheming on tail-less Vampires during this week and we have, I hope, contributed a little to progress.

These modest day-to-day words in fact described the birth of detailed design study on the first British aircraft to attain the speed of sound, the swept wing, tailless, de Havilland 108 (Photograph 24).

When the results of wartime German aerodynamic research became known, de Havilland's management quickly decided that the use of swept wings for high Mach number flight should be investigated at once. Wind-tunnels could achieve little immediately over and above existing German work, so the possibility of conducting full-scale, piloted flight research attracted their attention from both the military and commercial standpoints. In any case the new British wind-tunnels were not yet available.

De Havilland had already accumulated considerable experience of the lower transonic regions with their own straight winged jet fighter, the Vampire, and a quick way of producing a swept wing research aircraft seemed therefore to be at hand. Remove the wings from a standard Vampire fuselage and fit swept wings in their place; a solution which was not only adopted but even taken a stage further by making the resulting design tailless. This latter feature stemmed of course from the general obsession for reducing drag by dispensing with conventional tail units. In conformity with this thinking de Havilland therefore drew up plans for the Type 108. It was an ambitious, brave, individual, and eventually tragic

Photograph 24. The third de Havilland 108 VW.120. This aircraft, flown by the late John Derry, was the first British aircraft to exceed the speed of sound (6 September 1948).
(British Aerospace)

concept, but it fired the imagination and enthusiasm of the whole aircraft industry during the first intoxicating years of the supersonic age.

Some aerodynamic data had been obtained from experimental swept wing gliders at the low speeds needed for landing, so de Havilland combined the results of these with what was known of transonic airflow to outline a general arrangement of their proposed high-speed research aeroplane.

Drawings were sent to the RAE Farnborough and conversations held between de Havilland engineers and Mr W. G. A. Perring and Dr Douglas, the Director and Head of the Aerodynamics Department of the RAE, respectively. These resulted in a letter being sent on 27 July 1945, to Miss F. Bradfield, Head of the RAE Small Wind Tunnels Department, requesting tunnel facilities for '108' models. In a reply on 8 August 1945, de Havilland were informed that although formal sanction for such work had not yet been obtained from the Director of Technical Development, they could proceed on the assumption that authority would be forthcoming. A further request for any reports dealing with aspects of tailless aircraft behaviour produced a list of relevant publications, and on 10 August 1945, a letter was written to the Ministry of Aircraft Production of which the following is an extract.

> We should be much obliged if you would kindly obtain and forward us copies of the reports given on the attached list. We are investigating tail-less aircraft and have obtained this list from Miss H. M. Lyon of R.A.E.

So, after barely three months of peace in Europe the de Havilland Aircraft Company had started on the way to producing what became Britain's first serious competitor in the new, but worrying, supersonic world.

Events moved swiftly to finalize details of the 108 design. At a meeting in the Ministry of Aircraft Production, Thames House, London, on 21 November 1945, to discuss the 'Experimental Vampire with swept back wings', some clear definitions and decisions were minuted. Among other things it was learned:

> The intention is to provide a means whereby full scale flight experiments may be made to explore the possibilities of high speed tail-less aircraft with swept wings.
>
> No space for pilot ejection is possible without modifications to the standard Vampire fuselage. Although the Ministry of Aircraft Production would like to see such ejection on this aircraft it was agreed that the urgency of the aircraft would preclude the necessary fuselage and cockpit re-design. Aerodynamic load distribution across a wing should be investigated as a primary object. This is best accomplished by pressure plotting.

Pressure plotting required considerable instrumentation to measure pressure at numerous points on the wing surface. Thus the 108 work was to be in the category of controlled scientific experiment rather than a reckless attempt merely to achieve a given speed for its own sake. In fact, the original specification, a simple document compared with those issued today, called for a speed of 650 miles/h and a Mach number of 0·9, figures which were, even then, realistic.

During the second half of 1945 work on the 108 proceeded apace. Two machines were under construction having the serial numbers TG.283 and TG.306, the fuselages of both being standard Vampire units off the English Electric production line. The first of these was intended to investigate primarily low-speed effects. To the second, TG.306, fell the task of exploring the high Mach number regions. Salient features of the design were:

Wing area   328 ft²

Wing span   39 ft

Thickness/chord ratio   12·6% at root

10·0% outboard of duct

10·0% at tip

Dihedral   Nil

Sweepback angle   40 degrees

Fin and rudder (net area)   21 ft²

Sweepback   48 degrees

Engine   de Havilland Goblin (3000 lb static thrust initially)

Separate elevators were not fitted but an elevon, i.e., combined elevator and aileron, was positioned at each wing tip. These controls were not at first power operated. Leading edge slots were located on the outboard wing panels of both TG.283 and TG.306, being fixed open on the former and automatic on the latter. Apart from this difference, both machines were identical in all but minor details.

By May 1946, TG.283 was ready to fly – barely ten months after the first design calculations had been made. At this time no concrete runways were available at de Havilland's own airfield at Hatfield so initial flying of the 108 was undertaken at the Royal Air Force emergency airfield at Woodbridge in Suffolk. The late Geoffrey de Havilland, Jr, then Chief Test Pilot of the firm, was to make the first flight, and on 11 May 1946, he made a short hop. Wheelbrake trouble, however, prevented anything more exciting on this occasion.

On 15 May 1946, the 108 finally became airborne for the first time. Shortly afterwards, the second aircraft, TG.306, also flew. It was soon apparent that the configuration of the 108 produced flying characteristics at both high and low speeds which differed considerably from the conventional straight winged aircraft previously flown. At low speeds, with particular reference to the approach and landing, it was found difficult to execute a precise approach path, which tended to be shallow. When the rate of descent had been checked there was a tendency for the

100

aircraft to float. Greater drag from flaps would have helped but as we have mentioned earlier the resulting trim changes were difficult to control on an aeroplane without a separate horizontal tail surface.

The higher-speed trials involving TG.306 soon produced a wealth of fascinating data. The basic plan was first to investigate high indicated airspeeds, second to investigate high Mach numbers, and, finally, a combination of both.

Good progress was made in the early stages. Table 3 shows the speeds and Mach numbers achieved at the outset.

Table 3

Flight number	Indicated airspeed (miles/h)	Mach number	Height (ft)
3	595	0·82	3000
	595	0·845	4500
4	340	0·895	34 000
	340	0·89	35 000
5	450	0·86	19 000
6	595	0·86	5000
	615	0·85	3000
7	630	0·855	1500

The familiar nose down trim change as lift was reduced, was observed at a Mach number of 0·88 and increased up to 0·895, the highest value attained during these early flights. An expected loss of aileron power above 600 miles/h was not noticed.

On the performance side it was clear that compared with the Vampire, from which it was developed, and which had the same engine, the 108 was about 30 miles/h faster for a given engine thrust at low speeds – the difference being greater at high Mach numbers. Further improvement was subsequently obtained by redesigning the cockpit canopy, an action which also reduced some mild rudder buffeting.

Although considerable satisfaction was felt with the results of the early 108 flying there was unfortunately one most disturbing aerodynamic feature which was never eliminated throughout its lifetime. Above certain Mach numbers, the exact figure depending on height, a pitching oscillation developed which could become severe, as later experienced on the tailless, although slower, AW.52. The main danger here was that this effect did not necessarily give the pilot any warning but could commence suddenly, allowing little time to reduce speed. Any attempt to stop the oscillations with the control column was liable to make the situation worse. What is known as a pilot induced oscillation could then make the total motion so violent that abandoning the aircraft might be impossible. Describing the situation, eventually, in a report, these words were written by the firm's aerodynamics department:

> It became apparent at an early stage in the flight work on this aircraft that the short period pitching oscillation was not as well damped as on orthodox aircraft.

There was, however, one feature of high Mach number flight on the 108 which happily ran contrary to the popular image of such work in that little or no buffeting was experienced. From a structural point of view this was a great relief and the pilots were spared unduly rough rides. But even at this stage there was no real thought of being able to exceed the speed of sound, and before this was possible, disaster struck.

As the autumn of 1946 approached, thoughts turned towards the Society of British Aircraft Constructors Display, which up to 1948 had been held at Radlett in Hertfordshire and was not then open to the general. public. Geoffrey de Havilland demonstrated the high-speed 108 TG.306 at the display on Friday, 13 September. On looking back, some might think that this traditionally unlucky combination of day and date cast a spell over both the pilot and aircraft, for exactly two weeks later, on Friday, 27 September 1946, TG.306 crashed, killing Geoffrey de Havilland during practice for a world speed record attempt. He was thirty-six years old.

Up to the time of this sad happening only a limited amount of information on the 108 programme had found its way into the press. Such as was written did not suggest that swept wings were of prime importance for supersonic flight in the immediate future. They were looked upon as a possible solution but no more. Even as late as 19 September 1946, an article on research aircraft in the magazine *Flight* did not greatly emphasize that the 108 was the first British swept wing design, and the following remarks were made:

> Since May 15th this year tests have been in progress with the de Havilland 108 high speed research aircraft, a type which reflects German technique in wing design but which uses a fuselage similar to that of the Vampire.

Perhaps the tradition of using swept back wings on previous tailless aircraft for reasons of balance rather than Mach number had given the 108 an already familiar look, but the Germans had in some ways stolen everybody's thunder in presenting the world with such a concept for transonic flight. The British had so often produced simple solutions to engineering problems but where high-speed research was concerned their thinking had been concerned for too long with the difficulties of laminar flow.

So for the time being de Havilland forged on alone and it soon became evident that the 108 might stand a good chance of breaking the existing speed record of 616 miles/h. This was then held by Great Britain through the efforts of the Royal Air Force High Speed Flight using Gloster Meteor aircraft.

Preparations to do this were thus made and included the fitting of a modified cockpit canopy and improvements in general external finish. On the fatal 27 September, Geoffrey de Havilland took off in TG.306 for an evening flight which was to be the final test before departing for Tangmere aerodrome in Sussex. This airfield, of Battle of Britain fame, was to be the operating base for his record attempt. Up to this time it had not been proposed to exceed a Mach number of 0·87 until powered controls were fitted for fear of experiencing the always dangerous pitching oscillations, but after better streamlining of the airframe for the record attempt a figure of 0·895 was achieved without any trouble. Such was the nature of the problem, however, that no guarantee of continued immunity could be expected.

Recognizing the narrow margin probably existing between safety and disaster, the purpose of the flight on 27 September was twofold. First to dive to a Mach number of 0·87 or to the onset of any dangerous characteristics, whichever came first. Second to fly level at high speed over the sea to check behaviour under near-record conditions. The sortie was never completed.

It was an ideal evening for the tests with little cloud or turbulence and the first test was to be made over the Thames Estuary. But when the aircraft was due to return there was no sign of it and when the low fuel reserves carried by such a machine must long have been exhausted the 108 had still not returned. It was clear that Geoffrey de Havilland must have landed away from base – or crashed. Then Air Traffic Control began to receive ominous messages. An aircraft had been seen to break up over the Thames Estuary, north-east of Gravesend, about twenty minutes after the 108 had taken off, and the wreckage soon proved to be that of TG.306. The body of Geoffrey de Havilland was found at Whitstable.

One can well imagine the scene at Hatfield on this occasion. A group of people to whom the team spirit meant everything gradually realizing that a king-pin of their team would never return. The first job then was, briefly, to mourn – the second to determine what had happened – the third to continue with research. Such was, and is, the pattern of test flying.

In early October 1946, Sir Geoffrey de Havilland, to whom had fallen the unpleasant task of planning the future of the work which had killed his own son, said that the show would go on, and that John Cunningham, then Chief Test Pilot of the de Havilland Engine Company, would succeed Geoffrey de Havilland, Jr, as Chief Test Pilot of the aircraft company.

The firm was soon requested to go ahead with the provision of a replacement machine for TG.306, the wreckage of which had been recovered and was being thoroughly examined. It was not at first clear what had happened although some instrumentation was salvaged which showed that a Mach number of 0·875 was achieved at 7500 feet. Naturally some detailed damage had been suffered by individual components but whether some of this was a contributory factor to the accident or arising from it took time to determine. We now know that the dreaded pitching oscillation was almost certainly the culprit and that contrary to much wild and uninformed speculation at the time, Geoffrey de Havilland had not been killed making a death or glory attempt to 'break the sound barrier'. This would have been out of keeping with his methods. The flight on TG.306 was not in fact the last entry in his log-book. He had intended making a later flight in another aircraft and, in anticipation, had entered up both sorties together. Neither, of course, was completed.

It should here be understood that TG.306, the high-speed 108, might not have been lost had it been fitted with a conventional tail like its straight winged predecessor, the Vampire, or its larger successor, the deH.110 fighter (which we shall discuss in Chapter 5). The main culprit was not speed or Mach number but the lack of a tail to damp out pitching oscillations which could be induced in several ways, of which flying near the speed of sound was only one.

The matter of a tail was in fact considered for continuing the 108 programme and no time was lost in preparing a third 108, which received the serial number VW.120. A meeting was held at Thames House,

May 1946	deH.108 first flew.
December 1946	Bell X-1 made first powered flight but not with all rockets firing.
October 1947	Bell X-1 made first-ever flight faster than sound but only $M = 1.06$ achieved.

It has been said that the M52 was 90 per cent complete at the time of cancellation but this is open to question. Even if true, it is difficult, knowing the development problems of subsequent advanced aircraft, to imagine a first flight much before late 1946. From then on the need to increase speed in small steps as a precaution against flutter, if for no other reason, would have ruled out a supersonic flight by the M52 before about August 1947 and only then if all had gone well. In other words the best the M52 might have done was to beat the X-1 by a mere two months and this would probably have required a degree of luck almost unknown in such work.

The deH.108, on the other hand, first flew a full seventeen months before the Americans broke the barrier with the X-1, and the high-speed 108 achieved $M = 0.9$ on only its fourth flight. Admittedly the M52 was designed for considerably greater speeds but for the purpose of exceeding the speed of sound by the small margin necessary to record a 'first', it now seems clear that a modified deH.108, backed by a full-scale national effort, could have done the job. But, as we have said, this simply was not a British priority. So it remains to emphasize that of the early experimental aircraft which could have been first to exceed the speed of sound the deH.108 was certainly the first to fly.

5

NEW SHAPES FOR OLD

We have talked so far largely of experiments both on the ground and in the air – experiments aimed at obtaining data and experience rather than towards the production of a specific aircraft. Now let us look at some byproducts of these experiments and the events, people, and places involved.

In 1950 the re-equipment of the Royal Navy and Royal Air Force with modern British-designed aircraft still seemed tantalizingly far away and the understanding of transonic flight, however imperfect, was focused for a time on the development of new fighters. Aerodynamic investigation using ground-based simulators and component testing in environmental laboratories, both of which are commonplace today, were methods hardly born, so the majority of design deficiencies still had to await airborne experiments for solution.

The diversity of testing work necessary to perfect an aircraft was, however, increasing enormously with each small rise in Mach number, and this trend emanated mainly from the difficulty in predicting control behaviour. A direct, practical, result was therefore a demand for more prototype aircraft, so that various aspects of a trials programme could proceed concurrently.

This was a new approach to development work and did not suit such times of stringent economy, so British engineers had to make do for a while with limited numbers of experimental aircraft, a situation calling for their traditional abilities of ingenuity and improvisation. But as the 1950s wore on these abilities were for once unable to guarantee for Britain a world position – in this case as an aviation power – and her production lines continued to turn out types of military aircraft conceived in basic form ten years previously. Although these had considerable value as export and licence-built items they did not, even in modified form, match the more advanced products of other countries.

116

Overshadowing all other considerations was, of course, the presence of atomic weapons, and in particular the vulnerability of the British Isles to this form of attack. The ability of even the most up-to-date fighter force to destroy totally an enemy air fleet carrying nuclear bombs was questionable, and as the dropping of only two or three atomic or hydrogen bombs on such a small area seemed potentially catastrophic, why, it could be asked, should any effort be devoted to the large-scale production of fighters? Were not bombers in a deterrent role a better safeguard? The Royal Air Force understood the use of bombers as well as anybody, but until Bomber Command was reconstituted with jet aircraft it could only be hoped that American strength would counter the Russian threat. In the meanwhile, British squadrons suffered what to some was the temporary indignity of being equipped with American fighters and bombers.

As we have mentioned, however, the Korean conflict accelerated the production of both fighters and bombers with high Mach number, high-altitude capabilities, but, at first, these were of limited operational use for the simple reason that the radar devices intended to aid fighter interception and to ensure bombing accuracy were not available, having been planned for a much longer-term development. For a time, therefore, the Services possessed aircraft of modern performance whose function was limited to little more than flying training.

Civil aircraft development was continuing on sound lines but the dividends from this were very long term and for some years the aircraft involved could contribute little even to transonic flight knowledge.

The year 1951 thus opened with expectations of seeing some result for the recent high-speed research, and before the close of the year four important prototypes of fighter aircraft made their first flights.

In chronological order these were the Hawker Hunter (20 July 1951), Supermarine Swift (1 August 1951), de Havilland 110 (26 September 1951), and Gloster Javelin (26 November 1951). The Hunter and Swift were single-seat fighters, each powered by a Rolls-Royce Avon engine (Photographs 27a and b). The de Havilland 110 and Javelin were twin-engined two-seat fighters with Rolls-Royce Avon and Armstrong-Siddeley Sapphire engines, respectively (Photographs 28a and b). All four could exceed $M=1$ in a dive, and while none of them represented a major aerodynamic advance compared with the progress in the United States, their ability to make supersonic bangs attracted enormous interest from the general public.

117

Photograph 27a. Hawker Hunter – the first prototype WB.188.
(British Aerospace)

Photograph 27b. Supermarine Swift. The first production aircraft WJ.965. In this view the planform of the wing can be compared with that of its predecessors, the Types 510 and 535 shown in Chapter 3.
(Supermarine–Vickers Limited)

Photograph 28a. The de Havilland 110 swept wing two-seat Fighter which was developed into the Sea Vixen for the Royal Navy.
(British Aerospace)

Photograph 28b. Gloster Javelin all-weather Fighter. The world's first operational delta aircraft.
(British Aerospace)

In Chapter 3 we read of the research leading up to these four machines and we shall now see how they emerged from the experimental stage; but whatever judgement history may pass on their eventual achievements nobody will deny that their pilots were idolized and that names such as Lithgow, Duke, Cunningham, Derry, Morgan, and Waterton became everyday words. The whole country identified itself with the efforts of such men to put Britain back on the supersonic map, aeronautical magazines were full of vacancy notices for engineers, and lectures dealing with any aspect of supersonic flight invited the most intense discussion.

It is, therefore, thought appropriate in this chapter to deal not so much with policies as with personalities and places. For this purpose let us first go to Winchester, ancient capital of England and a renowned Cathedral city. Within a radius of twenty-five miles lie some of the jewels of English history – Stonehenge, Salisbury Cathedral, Romsey Abbey. To the north-west is the village of Stockbridge, situated in the valley of the River Test and famed for its fishing. Slightly to the north-east of Stockbridge lies another, smaller, village – Chilbolton, picturesque and far removed from the complexity of modern living, but life there was not always quiet. From 1947 to 1957 Chilbolton Aerodrome, a wartime creation perched on top of downs overlooking the village, was the centre of flight testing activity for Supermarines, or to give the organization its full title, Vickers-Armstrongs (Supermarine) Limited. The rest of the firm was far flung. Following the wartime bombing of its traditional home at Woolston in Southampton, the design offices of Supermarines had settled in a magnificent country house at Hursley Park, between Winchester and Romsey. Production facilities had been set up in a modern factory at South Marston, near Swindon, and other production work continued in Southampton and Trowbridge. A significant proportion of the Wiltshire and Western Hampshire population was thus directly concerned or associated with the welfare of Supermarine. To some the name was magic, to others it merely signified excessive noise. It is now, unfortunately, only something to mourn, but in 1950 the outlook was encouraging. At Chilbolton new prototype aircraft were awaited with enthusiasm which was one of the few assets the Chilbolton community possessed apart from an attractive location. A small, new, office building erected to house the pilots and technical staff was in some respects worthy of modern engineering, but the airfield runways were in a rough condition and barely suitable for operating high-performance experimental aircraft. Runway lengths of 1800 yd, 1600 yd, and 1400 yd were available although the longest of these, in one direction, ran downhill towards the Test Valley. The surrounding area, consisting of sharply undulating and partly wooded country, was a nightmare in the event of forced landing, but three or four remarkable emergency landings were made by Attacker and Swift aircraft during flights from Chilbolton, none of which caused serious injury to the pilot.

Compared with the extensive Flight Test facilities available in America where airfields several miles in length could be laid out, Chilbolton, in relation to its function, was most inadequate; but, by a combination of flying skill and technical expertise, a prolonged high-speed flight test programme was conducted there on various aircraft over a period of some ten years. Life was not always easy. In a place so isolated the recruitment and transfer of personnel was a major problem, and the critical housing shortage made matters worse for the married staff. Some in desperation solved the difficulty by the then popular practice of 'squatting', which meant taking over derelict service camps. Old RAF huts on the domestic sites at Chilbolton came into this category and were duly occupied by the families of numerous Supermarine engineers. Neither local authorities nor the Air Ministry encouraged this practice and, to limit the invasion, stupidly removed the doors and windows of other huts to prevent occupation. This, at a time when the country could ill-afford even the slightest hindrance to the building up of a modern Air Force. Eventually, when Supermarine's needs at Chilbolton became too obvious to be denied, steps were taken to approve the presence of its squatters. A group of highly qualified engineers thus graduated from the criminal classes to a somewhat higher status.

While such nonsense was being allowed to persist in Britain, more was being learned of the progress made by the American swept wing fighter, the F.86 Sabre, which became cloaked in such a mantle of virtue as to be known throughout the aircraft industry as 'That Aircraft'. It seemed way ahead of its rivals and within the scope of current knowledge the Americans had tackled its development on direct and vigorous lines, but although British fighters were able to match the F.86 in speed it was some time before they could compete in the detail design of such things as cockpit equipment, control, and electrical systems.

The appearance in 1948 of Supermarine's Type 510 had seemed to herald the reawakening of British aircraft design, but changing the Swift into an interim operational fighter brought unexpected difficulties. The

121

use of a modified Attacker fuselage had helped of course to reduce the cost of design and manufacture, and the time between contract signing and first flight was only twenty-one months. Two features, however, restricted its potential, these being the tiny, much criticized Attacker-type cockpit and its tail wheel layout. Cockpit equipment was increasing with the growing complexity of aircraft systems and the 510, as it stood, barely offered enough room for the pilot. The tail down ground attitude made cross-wind landing difficult and the tendency for tail wheel aircraft to bounce on landing meant that brakes might not be applied immediately after touch-down. As landing speeds and runs were greatly increasing, the days of tail wheels on high-speed aircraft ended with the coming of the jet engine and the need for more powerful, effective, and immediate braking.

To have any chance of becoming an operational fighter the Supermarine 510 therefore needed a nosewheel layout, and we mentioned in Chapter 3 how this change was made on the second 510 to produce the Type 535. In its new guise and with the serial number VV.119, it first flew on 1 September 1950. At this time only the Hawker 1067 (later to be called the Hunter) was being officially constructed as a transonic day fighter for the Royal Air Force, but orders for a swept wing fighter were possible from a foreign government and Supermarine were naturally interested. The absence of a Supermarine successor to the Spitfire for Britain's own defence was, however, a constant source of frustration within the firm.

To advertise their current efforts Supermarine installed reheat in VV.119 when still in its tail-wheeled form. The idea was to capture the world's speed record and extra fuel tankage was added to feed the thirsty reheat. It was soon apparent that the fuel consumption had been underestimated but by then the work of turning the aircraft into a fighter left no time for record breaking. So, equipped with a lengthened nose to accommodate a nosewheel and with reheat still on board, VV.119 was ready for flight only four months after work on the conversion started.

The reheat was not completely ignored and some preliminary tests of this, the only reheated Nene installation to fly, included telemetry measurements of turbine shaft loads. The system was, of course, in its infancy and could not be fully exploited immediately, so the extra weight and complication was eventually removed in the interests of other trials.

When it arrived at Chilbolton in 1950, VV.119 was, despite its contemporary appearance, a comparatively simple machine. Cockpit instruments were little more advanced than those of World War II, and with a fixed tailplane and manually operated elevators too much could not be expected where really high Mach number flying was concerned. Nevertheless, it was, with the Type 510, a useful introduction to swept wing research and a means of keeping Supermarine in the high-speed market.

As the test programmes on the Supermarine Types 510 and 535 progressed, any satisfaction derived from probing high Mach number flight was overshadowed by the runaway lead being established in this field by the Americans, even allowing for their superior numbers and economic strength. One incident in particular cast an air of gloom over the Chilbolton team, this being the visit of two F.86 Sabres operated by the Royal Canadian Air Force from RAF Station North Luffenham in Rutland. Arriving one morning the Sabre pilots were whisked off to lunch at a well-known hotel in Stockbridge. While they were absent, a party of designers and photographers from Hursley Park swarmed over the Sabres to study their construction and it was soon realized that this splendid aircraft was of very high quality, an opinion reinforced by a flying display laid on by the Canadians in the afternoon, at a time, it must be remembered, when Britain was still without an operational transonic aircraft. One of the Sabres, having taken off with the intention of aiming a supersonic bang at Chilbolton, returned after a few minutes, landed, and taxied in with a loose fuselage side panel which covered the gun compartment and which must have been partly loose on arrival. On this occasion, instead of guns, certain spare articles of pilots' clothing were carried, including a pair of trousers. The trousers had gone but the pilot, without stopping his engine, merely requested the offending panel to be secured, a simple process performed by tightening half a dozen fasteners. Again the Sabre took off and a loud bang was duly heard at Chilbolton about twenty minutes later. This in itself may not seem remarkable but the ease with which the demonstration proceeded left a profound impression on the audience. Why, it was asked, was the Swift still struggling to do something that the Sabre took in its stride? Why could the Americans quickly attach fuselage panels by a few simple fasteners when the Swift needed a large bagful of screws? Was this playing too safe?

In the search for excuses to explain away a disturbing situation some of the younger British aircraft designers cast a critical eye over their superiors. The creators of many a famous pre-war and wartime aircraft had come from an older school of draughtsman-designer, in some cases

123

lacking the higher academic qualifications demanded in later years, but were this older generation losing the art of innovation or was the country really unable to afford even a few advanced aircraft? This was of course no time to be holding an inquest so there was nothing for it but to make the best of what was available, and at Chilbolton, as elsewhere, efforts continued, spurred on to some extent by the 'Super-Priority' scheme. The Services, being aware of their own shortcomings, pressed strongly for replacements, and a dangerous attitude developed which regarded anything as better than nothing. The jet fighter specifications for the period under review certainly did not demand enough. In a few years bombers were going to be in service capable of speeds and heights equal to or greater than those possessed by contemporary fighters. Still more thrust was required from jet engines if the performance and high-altitude manoeuvrability of fighters was to be sufficient to catch the bombers.

The Supermarine 535 itself lacked power, a feature plainly apparent by its long take-off run. It also lacked an adequate fuel reserve and, in an effort to increase the fuel capacity, tests with an under fuselage drop tank were made. With this tank fitted, but empty, the take-off consumed every yard of the longest Chilbolton runway – a most hair-raising sight – and when further tests with a full drop tank were considered, calculations showed that with the increased weight and drag the chances of getting airborne, even on the 3000-yd-long runway of Boscombe Down, were marginal.

The question of how to develop the Type 535 was then unexpectedly solved by the outbreak of war in Korea. At this time the Hunter was a year away and nobody could predict its suitability as a fighter. An emergency decision was therefore taken at a secret meeting in the Ministry of Supply to produce a fully equipped fighter version of the Supermarine 535 as a back-up for the Hunter programme and an insurance against its failure.

It was obvious that a more powerful engine would be needed, and although the Rolls-Royce Avon was selected, it was thought that a supply shortage might require the first few aircraft to retain the Nene. As a start, an aircraft almost identical to VV.119 was nevertheless equipped with an Avon of 7500 lb thrust, this representing a 50 per cent increase. Having the serial number WJ.960 and Type number 541, this machine was the first of the real Swift range, although for some time the name Swift had unofficially been given to both the Types 510 and 535.

An increase of power was not, however, the only modification needed to give the Swift a fighting capability. A new cockpit was essential as were detailed changes to the fuselage and wings, but pending this redesign much basic aerodynamic testing was completed with WJ.960. The first flight was made from Boscombe Down in August 1951. Control vibrations were experienced on early tests due to mechanical rather than aerodynamic deficiencies, and one such outbreak, on the third flight, caused the fuel-cock linkage to break and the engine to stop. The pilot on this occasion was M. J. Lithgow who managed to land without damage at Chilbolton.

A greatly improved performance resulted from the new engine, and although the outdated fixed tailplane and elevator control system remained, it was not this but the aileron control which prevented WJ.960 from achieving $M=1$ in a dive. In early form the ailerons had spring tabs and were prone to flutter at high Mach numbers; a spring by its nature not being a rigid device. No design change was initially contemplated so the Swift stayed, for the time being, a subsonic aeroplane, but the fitting of the variable incidence tailplane scheduled early in the testing life of WJ.960 went some way to modernizing the design. As it happened, the aircraft was lucky to survive to see it. On 8 September 1951, only three days before the Farnborough Show, WJ.960, flown by D. W. Morgan, crashed on the approach to Chilbolton following engine failure. Morgan was too low to eject but made a magnificent and successful effort to save the aircraft which, although suffering damage to the tail, was capable of being repaired. In about three months it was flying again and the opportunity was soon taken to fit the variable incidence tail with which it made its first flight in February 1953. The day after his crash Morgan, who was uninjured, flew the Type 535 on a pre-Farnborough Show photographic sortie as the 535 once more had to represent Supermarine at the Show. In passing it should be mentioned that some early experience with variable incidence tailplanes had been gained on the first Type 510, VV.106. This was modified to a Type 517 by the fitting of an unusual rear fuselage, the whole of which was hinged to rotate in the vertical plane by a few degrees up and down. The relevant design work was undertaken by Tiltman Langley Laboratories Limited, the final contrivance being first flown by M. J. Lithgow on 12 December 1951.

Despite the intensive flight test programme a supersonic flight by a Swift was, however, long in coming and was eventually needed as much for prestige as for technical purposes.

Over at Dunsfold, in Surrey, Hawkers had dived a Hunter faster than sound, but the Spitfire builders, by retaining an unsuitable aileron system, denied themselves this same privilege. Then came a visit to England of General Al Boyd of the United States Air Force, whose job was to assess British fighter aircraft for purchase on behalf of the North Atlantic Treaty Organization (NATO). He flew a Hunter supersonically but could not, at that time, do the same in a Swift, a situation emphasizing the urgency of Swift development which in fact was about to reach its first climax.

Following the fatal crash of a de Havilland 110 at the 1952 Farnborough Show, concern increased for the structural integrity of transonic aircraft and, in particular, for the failures which could be caused by flutter. Accordingly the first fully representative Mark 1 Swift, WJ.965, having just flown on 18 July 1952, was grounded in the third quarter of 1952 for the installation of additional test instrumentation, a job which Supermarine instrument engineers always did extremely well (Photograph 29).

Photograph 29. Scene inside Supermarine's experimental hangar at Chilbolton in the early 1950s. In the foreground is the first production aircraft WJ.965, specially instrumented for flight vibration work. Note bulges on fin containing cameras to photograph wool tufts on rear fuselage. Other cameras photographed the wings. In background the Type 535 VV.119 and other production Swifts.
(Supermarine–Vickers Limited)

An intensive test flying programme then started on 22 November 1952, during which cine films were obtained of aileron and wing flutter at high speeds low down. This was more severe than had been experienced on the prototype WJ.960, and was the result of reducing the wing skin thickness· in an effort to save weight. The effect at high altitude was less severe, the air loads of course being reduced in the thinner air.

(AUTHOR'S NOTE: I had the job of analysing these films from WJ.965. The first film was horrifying – the whole wing seemed to disappear in a mist of vibration. I rang the pilot Dave Morgan and said, 'Dave, you'd better come and see this'. He looked and was appalled; but a closer examination revealed that vapour had formed over the top surface of the wing – a common occurrence, making the vibration look far worse than it was – although it was still bad enough.)

The outcome of these tests was the removal of the spring tab ailerons and their replacement by a geared tab type. This more rigid system was first flown on 18 February 1953, fitted to WJ.965, and one week later, on 26 February, it enabled this aircraft to deliver, to the delighted Chilbolton staff, the first supersonic bang to be heard from a Swift. The pilot on this occasion was also D. W. Morgan, who thought he might have exceeded the speed of sound some four days earlier: in fact it was almost certain. During a dive the needles of his airspeed indicator, altimeter, and machmeter had given a flick, indicating the movement of a shock wave over the external pressure head – a sure sign that the speed of sound had been exceeded. The machmeter pressure errors had not, however, been fully determined so it could not be confirmed until a bang was heard.

But as the excitement of listening to home-produced supersonic bangs gradually diminished, the Supermarine team found itself in desperate trouble. The Mark 1 Swifts had been equipped to carry two 30 mm cannons, but this fire power had to be doubled. Now the guns themselves were carried in the lower fuselage but their ammunition was stored in the wing roots, and to accommodate the extra rounds for four guns the wing inboard leading edge had to be extended forward (Fig. 10). The first four-gun version was the Mark 2 and the new wing shape proved disastrous. It changed the airflow pattern so that an uncontrollable manoeuvre known as 'pitch-up' occurred when 'g' was applied at Mach numbers of about 0·85 or above. What happened was this. The pilot pulled the stick back and applied a certain amount of 'g' – he pulled a bit

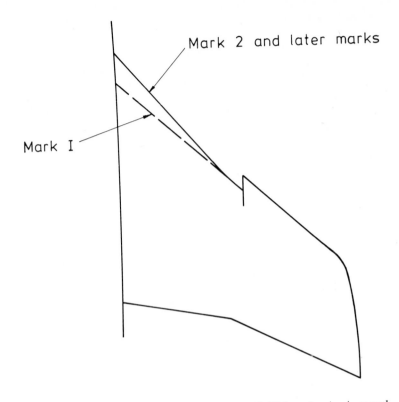

Mark 2 and later marks

Mark I

Figure 10. Plan view of wing of Supermarine Swift Fighter showing increased sweepback introduced on the Mark 2. This caused the nose to pitch up uncontrollably during turns at high altitude and was responsible for the Swift being cancelled as a Fighter.

harder and suddenly the nose reared up so rapidly that immediate forward movement of the stick could not arrest the motion. As a result, the aircraft could flick over on to its back, a situation totally unacceptable for a fighting machine when the pilot was trying to follow an enemy.

The Swift was not alone in displaying this effect but did so to an excessive degree and various wing modifications were tried with partial success. Wing 'fences' were added to the top surface of the wing, these being a sort of breakwater to prevent the outflow of air towards the wing tip, which was prone to flow breakaway. The leading edges of the outer wings were extended forward in a manner now common on many swept wing aircraft; this effectively reduced the surface curvature and was also intended to prevent flow breakaway. In the end, however, the centre of gravity had to be moved much farther forward than originally intended. To do this a few hundred pounds of extra lead ballast were fitted in the nose of the early models, but this added weight reduced the Swift's high altitude performance to such an extent that it could not be regarded as first line equipment – at least not in the high altitude bracket.

Following the Mark 1 and the Mark 2 came the Mark 3, equipped with reheat, and then the intended production version, the Mark 4, which incorporated not only the major features of the earlier marks but also the long-awaited variable incidence tailplane which it had been hoped might help to control the 'pitch-up'. Activity then reached a crescendo at Chilbolton as test flying went on seven days a week. The local population did not take kindly to the continual roar of jet aircraft and extreme wrath was justifiably expressed whenever ground running of the engine reheat system was undertaken. The noise generated by these runs reached unbearable levels and, on occasions, reheat tests on the ground were heard at great distances from Chilbolton. This was before the days of exhaust noise mufflers.

(AUTHOR'S NOTE: I remember one still, clear, summer's night in 1953 when playing tennis in the outskirts of Southampton, a jet aircraft reheat system could be heard in the distance being switched on and off during what was obviously an engine ground running test. The time of this incident was noted (about 8 p.m.) and on arriving at Chilbolton for work the next day a quick check with the ground crew confirmed that the first Mark 4 WK.198 had in fact been performing reheat ground runs at this time. We had heard the noise at a range of seventeen miles, and others claimed to have heard it even farther away.)

As if the aerodynamic trouble wasn't enough, however, the Swift also suffered trouble with the engine. In mid-1953 compressor blade failures started to occur, leading in some cases to complete engine seizure. Under these circumstances it was not easy to land at speeds approaching 150 miles an hour, and although ejection would have been a justifiable action by the pilot, Lithgow and his team knew that Swifts were scarce. The consequences of losing an aircraft at that stage would have been incalculable so the Supermarine pilots took the risk more than once of bringing a Swift back to earth without power.

These engine failures were curious in that Hawkers were not experiencing the same trouble in Hunters although using what should have been the same engine. On the face of it Supermarine's engine air intake design seemed suspect and numerous theories produced equally numerous changes in intake layout – all to no avail. A frantic period of intensive flying was then undertaken over a period of some weeks before Rolls-Royce realized that the engines in the Hunter and the Swift were not, after all, quite the same. A slightly different compressor design had found its way into the Swift and modifications had to be made to the compressor blade roots. The failures then ceased but only after a grand finale on no less an occasion than the Coronation review flypast on 15 July 1953. Included in this event was a token formation of the five available Swifts, thereby introducing a touch of home-made modernity to an otherwise ageing force. Four were Mark 1s flown by Royal Air Force pilots operating from Boscombe Down, the remaining aircraft being the prototype Mark 4 WK.198, flown by M. J. Lithgow. As the problem of compressor failure was then unsolved all five machines were fitted with brand-new engines, this action being unfortunately the only precaution possible. Even then no guarantee could be given that these pitifully few swept wing fighters would not disgrace the scene by suffering engine failures in full view of Her Majesty the Queen. As it happened the worst fears were nearly realized. After the flypast, Lithgow, in the Mark 4 Swift suffered engine compressor blade failure followed by seizure when fortunately near Chilbolton. He force-landed without damage or injury but it had been a very narrow escape!

The year 1953 was in fact a busy one for the prototype Mark 4. In addition to undergoing an arduous test programme it took part in the Farnborough Show and then, as if to reward Supermarines for three years of almost unbroken worry, went immediately to North Africa and broke the World's Absolute Speed record by returning 735·7 miles/h, only to lose the record within days to the American Douglas Skyray.

But despite a massive development effort the control problems of the Swift could not in the end be solved except by making the aircraft too heavy to operate as a high-altitude interceptor, and work on the Mark 4 was stopped in early 1955. From February 1954 number 56 Squadron, Royal Air Force, then based at Waterbeach in Cambridgeshire, had received a few Mark 1s and 2s, but after a brief career hedged around by numerous limitations they were withdrawn in May 1955.

A new requirement for a low-altitude fighter reconnaissance aircraft had nevertheless emerged and the Swift was modified to operate in this role as the FR.Mark 5. The Mark 5 was basically a Mark 4 but with a lengthened nose to contain cameras. About seventy of the type served with the Second Tactical Air Force in Germany and acquitted themselves well, being twice winners of the NATO low-level reconnaissance competition.

As an indication of what the Swift might have been, given time, the abilities of two late variants are of interest. A production Mark 4 Swift WK.275 was fitted with a slab tailplane and also with datum trimming. Supermarine test pilots described the resulting handling at high Mach numbers as superb. An even more extensive conversion involved a Mark 5 WK.308, this machine being fitted with not only a slab tail but also with extended wing tips, giving an increased wing area and a large diameter reheat jet pipe giving increased thrust. The ability of the Swift in this form can best be described in the words of D. W. Morgan, who first flew WK.308 in December 1955:

This aircraft was without question the best performer at high altitude and high Mach number in the country at the time, since, for the first time, we had one aeroplane with the three things most needed: increased wing span, a slab tail and the correct amount of thrust from a re-heated engine.

Twelve Swifts were subsequently produced having the increased wing span and the large jet pipe. Known as the Mark 7, they were used for guided weapon trials and of them Mr Morgan said:

In the hands of ordinary squadron pilots they were found to have an excellent capability as an interceptor carrying Fireflash guided weapons. It is no exaggeration to say that this aircraft/weapon combination was the best available to the Royal Air Force for years but was never put into service.

The end of Swift development also saw the end of Supermarine as an independent organization. In 1928 the firm had been acquired by Vickers and for many years its affairs had been substantially self-directed, but in the mid-1950s economies began to be needed in the British aircraft industry, and it was decided to close Chilbolton and move Supermarine's flight test activities to Vickers-Armstrongs' main base at Wisley in Surrey. This move took place in the summer of 1956 and was completed in time to begin the development of Supermarine's last design to fly, a swept wing

Photograph 30. The Scimitar Royal Navy Fighter. The last Supermarine design to fly. This is the first prototype WT.584 with special nose.
(Supermarine–Vickers Limited)

fighter for the Royal Navy known as the Type 544 Scimitar (Photograph 30).

Some preliminary work for the Scimitar had, however, been going on at Chilbolton for about four years. Two straight winged versions (Photograph 31), the Types 508 and 529, had first flown on 31 August 1951 and 29 August 1952, respectively, and, at the time, were the largest aircraft ever built for the Royal Navy. Both were powered by two Rolls-Royce Avon engines and both had butterfly tails, a layout intended to give protection to the rear structure when landing on inflatable bags – this idea having been dreamed up when jet aircraft landing speeds seemed likely to be too high for normal deck operations. In the event no unusual techniques proved necessary.

The 508 and 529 had a remarkable take-off performance compared with the prototype Swift (Type 535) and for some time a hint of either of them

Photograph 31. Supermarine 529. With its sister aircraft, the Type 508, this was a straight winged predecessor of the Scimitar. Note 'butterfly' tail. (Supermarine–Vickers Limited)

being about to fly caused the onlookers to gather, but the occurrence of wing flutter at an early stage put an unexpected limitation on their work. This did not, of course, affect low-speed tests, and in May 1952 the 508 performed aircraft carrier trials aboard HMS *Eagle*. Bearing in mind that the wings of the 508 and 529 were about nine per cent thick and were not intended for high supersonic speed, it is natural to speculate if flutter would have been a serious problem on the straight and even thinner winged Miles M52. Much less was then known about the subject and far less time was available to calculate what was known.

The swept wing prototype of the Scimitar, the Type 525, first flew from Boscombe Down on 28 April 1954, and was also tested at Chilbolton. It was fitted with flap blowing to reduce the deck landing attitude, giving the pilot a better view ahead. This machine was destroyed in an accident on 5 July 1955. The 525 and the production Scimitars were also equipped

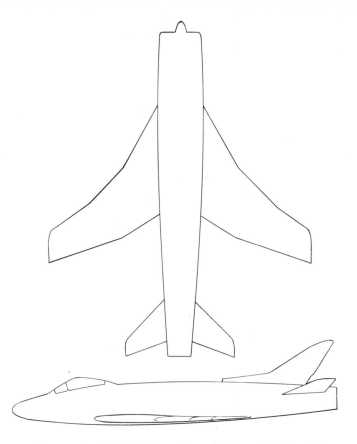

Figure 11. Supermarine 545. This aircraft was the last to be designed by Supermarines. Although the prototype was nearly completed it never flew.

with fully powered flying controls so at last there was becoming available the sort of transonic aeroplane which so many had tried and died to achieve. The Scimitar was in fact almost supersonic in level flight and if developed further could doubtless have had a much enhanced performance.

By way of a swan-song one other Supermarine design for a single-seat fighter was under construction in 1956. Known as the Type 545, it possessed a crescent wing similar to the ill-fated Handley-Page 88 and would have achieved a Mach number greater than 1·2 in level flight using a Rolls-Royce Avon engine with reheat. A handsome machine (Fig. 11), the 545 resembled a mixture of Swift, Scimitar, and Sabre, but like many other supersonic projects of similar vintage, it represented only a moderate advance on current types. The Lightning was by then flying, which as a design for almost twice the speed of sound offered the Royal Air Force an advance in performance sufficient to satisfy the needs of Fighter Command for at least ten years.

Pending the arrival of Lightnings, however, Britain's air defence depended on the successful development of Hawker's graceful fighter, the Hunter, and an intense rivalry between Supermarine and Hawker, from 1950 to 1955, left Hawker with a jet fighter which is still in demand by foreign powers. After its first flight at Boscombe Down in July 1951, the Hunter progressed through its initial trials with comparative ease. Speed and Mach number were increased by small steps as in the short summary of events shown in Table 6 covering this period.

Table 6

Dates	Highest Mach number reached	State of aircraft
20/7/51 (First flight)	0·6	Elevator booster inoperative
24/7/51– 17/8/51	0·875	
23/8/51– 8/10/51	0·915	Elevator booster operative (2·75 to 1)

(NOTE: For these flights the cabin pressure was not working. Extensive modification programme between 8 October 1951 and 9 January 1952 included:
  Elevator boost increased to 5 to 1
  Cockpit pressurization fitted
  Centring spring fitted to aileron controls)

9/1/52– 29/1/52	0·92	
30/1/52– 22/2/52	0·99	
23/2/52– 13/3/52	1·0 (Speed of sound)	

It will be seen that up to October 1951, the cabin pressurization system was inoperative and flight above 30 000 ft prohibited. This, of course, limited the Mach number attainable in a dive. Once the extensive modification programme between October 1951 and January 1952 had been completed, supersonic flight was quickly achieved, but, as in the case of the Swift, a bang (heard in Petworth area) was the first intimation of success.

Although less plagued by trouble than the Swift, perhaps not surprisingly as the Swift was a hastily conceived back-up aircraft, the Hunter was not, however, without its problems and in a Hawker report of 28 October 1952, it was stated:

> At an early stage in the flight development it was apparent to the pilots that an undesirable buffet was present at Mach numbers about 0·8. The severity of the buffet increased with Mach number reaching a peak at about 0·92 and reducing to mild proportions by 0·96. It occurred at all altitudes but became more intense with reduction in altitude until at 5000 ft and speeds associated with Mach numbers of the order of 0·9 it was unacceptably violent in amplitude.
>
> The pilots described it as starting with a vibration on the rudder pedals which built up in amplitude until the whole airframe was shaking.

The effect was worse at lower altitudes because the density of the air was greater, giving rise to greater loads – a feature which was mentioned earlier. The vibration of the rudder pedals suggested that the buffeting was coming from the tail rather than from elsewhere, but several changes made to the rear fuselage contours produced no improvement. The report then went on to say:

> The final cure to the buffet was obtained by the addition of a circular section rear bullet-type fairing at the intersection of the elevators and fin. Although RAE tunnel tests predicted no worthwhile improvement to be gained from such a fairing, the presence of this combined with the tail parachute container made the Hunter free of all buffet right through the transonic range.

Figure 12 shows this simple modification which was fitted to all Hunters. Similar fairings became common on other types as more was learned of transonic airflow and the whole business took on a less fearsome appearance than when first encountered. We noted in connection with the Spitfire wing thickness how tunnel tests could be misleading when dealing with particular aspects of transonic flow, and the Hunter buffet case was yet another indication of how, at that time, such problems could be solved with certainty only by using full-sized manned aircraft.

On the second Hunter prototype some mild elevator flutter was experienced but not of a serious nature and this was cured by balancing adjustments.

The Hunter flew supersonically exactly a year before the Swift, but the Swift was, nevertheless, the first to enter Squadron service, simply because the Hunter lacked an air brake, an item considered essential in fighter aircraft where the ability to slow down quickly can be as important as good acceleration. Some delay was, however, experienced in finalizing

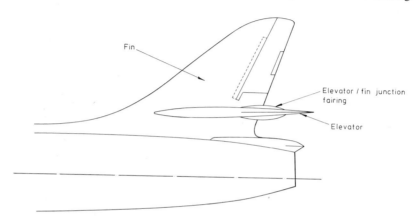

Figure 12. Hawker Hunter. This view of the tail assembly shows the simple elevator/fin junction fairing which eliminated the severe tail buffeting at high Mach numbers.

the air brake requirement and, in consequence, numerous Hunters lay scattered around Hawker's airfield at Dunsfold while an air brake system was tested.

Once cleared for service use, the Hunter then went from strength to strength, and all manner of weapons and other stores could be carried (Photograph 32). A two-seater version appeared and about 2000 were eventually built, but the general public probably remember this successful machine best for its remarkable formation aerobatic displays in the hands of 'Treble-One' Squadron when led by Squadron Leader Roger Topp (recently retired as Air Commodore).

Photograph 32. Hunter Mark 6. Despite carrying under wing stores the aircraft has changed little in appearance from the first prototype. Airbrake can be seen folded under rear fuselage.
(British Aerospace)

For ever associated with the Hunter will, however, be the name of Neville Duke, one-time Chief Test Pilot of Hawker Aircraft. Duke, who had a distinguished wartime record as a fighter pilot, eventually took the Empire Test Pilots School course but was no newcomer to high-speed flying, having been in the Royal Air Force High Speed team which broke the World's speed record shortly after the war, using a Gloster Meteor. One incident in his career, probably now forgotten by many, concerns the day on which John Derry and Tony Richards were killed following disintegration of their de Havilland 110 at the Farnborough Show in 1952. Neville Duke was scheduled to display the Hunter immediately following Derry's disastrous demonstration. While the dead and dying from among the crowd were being moved away, Duke took off. Climbing high above the airfield he aimed his Hunter towards Farnborough and unleashed a supersonic bang over the area. Seen by some as an unnecessary irreverence it was in fact a widely acclaimed action of which Derry himself would probably have approved and Sir Winston Churchill commended Duke for his spirit. They were days of adventure and the Show had to go on. When supersonic airliners entered service protests were registered in anticipation long before even one bang had been heard.

In 1952 the protestors were a minority. Supersonic bangs were then generally regarded as a national status symbol.

(AUTHOR'S NOTE: When the Swift was being evaluated at Boscombe Down, Squadron Leader P. D. Thorne (then a Test Pilot on 'A' Squadron and now retired as an Air Commodore), made what I calculated from his log-books to be 97 supersonic dives over a period of fifteen months on this type of aircraft alone, although not all were over land.)

Nowadays when the influence of mass publicity can cause contempt to precede familiarity, the noise made by supersonic airliners is not accepted with the gay abandon of the 1950s.

The Swift–Hunter contest dominated the British mid-century aviation arena to an extent which partly overshadowed the development of other high-speed aircraft. Another rivalry, however, developed between the de Havilland 110 and the Gloster GA.5 Javelin. Following experiences with swept wings on the deH.108, de Havilland had conceived the 110 as an advanced twin-engined Naval fighter to succeed their already ordered but straight winged Sea Vampire. Both were twin boom layouts, but when the RAF issued Specification F4/48 for an all-weather night fighter, the deH.110, which approximated to its requirements, was offered by de Havilland as a candidate. The plan form of the 110 in fact bears a striking resemblance to how the 108 would have looked had it been fitted, as once intended, with a twin boom tail. A development contract for two prototypes was signed. Gloster likewise received a contract for their competitor, the GA.5, a delta winged twin-engined layout.

Of these two aircraft, the deH.110 claimed the lion's share of publicity by virtue of its early ability to attain supersonic speeds and by having as pilot John Derry, already famous for his supersonic dives in the 108. But on paper the Javelin performance seemed to offer advantages, so the Javelin was ordered for the night fighter role in preference to the 110, which retraced its steps and was produced as a successful Naval fighter named Sea Vixen, but not, of course, before considerable re-design had taken place.

This led to the Javelin becoming the world's first operational delta winged aircraft when it joined No. 46 Squadron Royal Air Force, at Odiham, Hampshire, in February 1956. But the Javelin had not had an easy passage in the flight testing stages. On 29 June 1952, the first prototype, WD.804, had experienced elevator flutter under the dangerous combination of high speed and low altitude. Flown at the time by Gloster's Chief Test Pilot, W. A. Waterton, the elevators were torn away but Waterton managed to make an emergency landing at Boscombe Down, and although he survived, to be awarded the George Medal for his exploit, the valuable aircraft caught fire and was destroyed.

A further problem with the Javelin involved the 'superstall', later to become notorious with other aircraft having a tailplane mounted high on the fin. In these cases recovery from the stall could not be achieved by the normal technique of pushing the control column forward. Automatic stall, warning, or even stall prevention, devices were thus developed in preference to major redesign. One of Gloster's own test pilots, Peter Lawrence, was in fact killed after ejecting too late from a superstalled condition.

By 1959, the Swifts, Hunters, Javelins, and Sea Vixens were entering service in worthwhile numbers. They were large, complex and expensive aircraft by previous standards. A growing school of thought was thus considering ways to produce smaller, simpler, and more easily serviceable machines but still capable of supersonic speeds.

Among the British advocates of lightweight jet fighters was the late W. E. W. Petter, who, from 1950 to 1959, guided the fortunes of Folland Aircraft Limited in the capacity of Managing Director and Chief Engineer. Petter's career is described in several books. It is sufficient to say here that prior to joining Folland Aircraft he was successively Technical Director of Westland Aircraft and then Chief Engineer of English Electric Aviation Limited.

At Folland, Petter examined the concept of a lightweight fighter with a transonic performance equal to larger aircraft of corresponding role. The main requirement was for a small engine with a high thrust to weight ratio. Without this the project was not worth considering. Bristol-Siddeley Engines Limited were in fact developing a suitable unit, the Saturn, around which Petter and his team tailored, as a private venture, a diminutive swept wing fighter, having a weight less than half that of the Swift or Hunter.

140

The need to protect the British Isles from atomic attack at very short notice had led to studies of cheap, short life, or even expendable, interceptor fighters. These, if sent up in swarms, would, it was hoped, guarantee to destroy a bomber before the atomic weapon had been released: it was too late afterwards, and although the Folland team at one time considered this approach, their final design, called the Gnat, although very small, was more conventional. As it happened it nearly came to nothing when the Saturn engine was abandoned due to pressure of other work, but fortunately a slightly larger and more powerful engine, the Orpheus, was developed when it was seen that a market might soon exist for smaller engines quite apart from Folland's needs.

Considerable increases in aircraft size and weight had accompanied the change from piston to jet-propulsion engines. A higher structure weight was necessary to resist the increased drag loads of the much higher speeds and more space was needed for the complex armaments, navigational, and cabin pressurization systems. (The later Marks of Spitfire weighed about 9000 lb; the Swift anything from 14 000 to 18 000 lb.) It was therefore with some scepticism that designers viewed Petter's tiny machine which, at only about 6000 lb weight, was lighter than a Spitfire. Once the technique of producing small jet engines had been mastered there was really no reason why correspondingly small flying machines should not be built. But jet fighters were not just flying machines. They were becoming part of a rediscovered concept – the weapons system. Just as in days gone by when ancient earthworks and stone castles had been designed as integrated defence structures, so aircraft armament and anything that helped its function became part of a whole weapon package rather than a collection of separate guns or bombs stuck on an aeroplane.

Could a structure as small as the Gnat contain all the equipment needed to make up an advanced fighter? Originality and extreme economy of space were obviously needed. For instance, the undercarriage, when partly down, was used as an air brake, thus enabling the system to perform a dual function.

While Folland were preparing the Gnat designs, it was clear that the Orpheus engine would not be ready for the first aircraft, so a preliminary version, the Midge (Photographs 33a and b), was constructed, powered by an Armstrong-Siddeley Viper engine. This machine first flew on 11 August 1954, and provided invaluable advanced information. It was flown by numerous pilots other than Folland's own team but crashed on

Photograph 33a. Folland Midge. The Viper-powered prototype of the Gnat Fighter.
(British Aerospace)

Photograph 33b. A line-up of Gnat Fighters at Chilbolton in the mid-1950s.
(British Aerospace)

26 September 1955, after take-off, when being flown by a Swiss pilot who was unfortunately killed.

Prior to the start of Midge and Gnat flight testing, Folland had moved into Chilbolton aerodrome and shared life with Supermarine. They also found facilities primitive.

Eventually government interest in the Gnat was aroused and five development aircraft were ordered by the Ministry of Supply. It seemed that Folland were on the verge of a minor triumph and might, contrary to all expectations, secure a Royal Air Force or Royal Navy order. Official interest, however, meant official trials, and when the Gnat went to Boscombe Down for assessment, severe but justifiable criticisms were levelled at its tailplane and elevator control systems. This was tragic. For some years British designers had tried to extract the most from outdated controls, yet when Petter and his team attempted to design the Gnat on modern lines they were hoist with their own petard. The small size of the Gnat cockpit restricted the fore and aft movement of the control column, so, to move the tailplane through the desired range, a system using datum trimming was employed, whereby the control column was always in the central position when the aircraft was in trim.

This resulted in oversensitive control over part of the speed range. There were also some undesirable features in the design of the tailplane operating mechanism which caused a Boscombe Down pilot to eject and be killed when the ejection seat failed to work properly.

In the end, after bitter controversy, the Gnat was not considered suitable for Royal Air Force use. A most embarrassing situation meanwhile arose for the Ministry of Supply. Numerous foreign powers urgently required modern jet fighters. Hunters, Swifts, and their American counterparts were expensive both to buy and maintain. An aircraft such as the Gnat seemed therefore an attractive and cheaper substitute. Folland thus had the capacity to capture a valuable export market but, as frequently occurs in such circumstances, some sort of approval by an official testing establishment in the country of origin was required before other countries would place an order.

Desperate efforts were made to improve the Gnat control and eventually Boscombe Down, under great pressure, gave grudging approval to the design. They were not being 'head-in-sand' but they did have to test aircraft to a set of standards and the Gnat simply did not meet these in sufficient degree for Royal Air Force service. An order was nevertheless placed by the Indian Air Force. Twenty-five complete aircraft were delivered and fifteen sets of components supplied for assembly by Hindustan Aircraft Limited at Bangalore. Subsequently it was the intention of this company to build 100 Gnats under licence, but in 1965 this number was increased to 150. The Indians appear to have been satisfied and gave glowing accounts of the Gnat's abilities in battle.

In addition to the Indian sales, twelve Gnats were supplied to the Finnish Air Force and two to Yugoslavia.

Various developments of the basic Gnat were proposed, including a two-seat trainer version, which was offered to the Royal Air Force. After insisting on changes to the tailplane control system, the Ministry of Aviation tested and approved the Gnat Trainer (Photograph 34), which is still in service and has achieved fame by being selected as the equipment for the Red Arrows Aerobatic team. But in September 1959 Folland Aircraft was taken over by Hawker-Siddeley Aviation Limited, whose Hunter Trainer was once in competition with the two-seat Gnat, and although Hawker saw fit not to continue with the Folland line of designs, their recent Hawk Trainer owes its existence in no small way to the original Folland team.

Photograph 34. The Gnat Trainer. Two-seat development of the Gnat Fighter. The pilot in the cockpit gives some idea of the small size of these aircraft.
(British Aerospace)

Lightweight fighter designs in general and the Gnat projects in particular posed intriguing problems of crew escape. Existing ejector seats were too big or heavy for the small cockpits evolved so Folland adapted a simple Swedish seat for their needs and, as it happened, their own Chief Test Pilot, E. A. Tennant, was the first pilot to save his life using this miniature seat. When flying the first prototype Gnat on 31 July 1956 Tennant felt severe vibration. The tailplane had completely broken away following the onset of flutter, again at high speed and low altitude, but the aircraft flew on for about eight miles before the nature of the failure was fully appreciated. Ejection was inevitable but at that time the seat was completely unproven. Fortunately, it worked properly and Tennant landed safely to find later that parts of the tail had landed near his own home.

This was an interesting incident as it drew attention to a growing problem associated with aircraft control systems. It was not sufficient that each part of a system was alone stiff enough to withstand certain loads. When all parts were linked together a degree of flexibility might occur which reduced the stiffness of the circuit as a whole. An everyday example can, of course, be experienced on worn motor-car steering when juddering of the wheels is sometimes felt.

A Folland Aircraft report on the crash investigation was issued on 22 November 1956 (Aerodynamics Report No. 141/11), and in dealing with the pre-flight ground tests on flutter it said:

> The significant feature of this clearance procedure is that no suspicion was aroused that the tail attachment lacked stiffness.

and of the investigations made after the crash it was stated:

> When tail flutter was first suspected, the original calculations used for the clearance were examined and flutter was seen to be a possibility if considerable reduction in rotational stiffness had occurred on the tailplane.

Rotational stiffness meant the stiffness of the whole tailplane actuating system as opposed to the torsional stiffness of the tailplane alone.

It was further stated that:

> Static stiffness measurements were therefore made in considerable detail to determine the contribution to the overall flexibility of the various parts of the tail actuating system.

145

The tests showed that the stiffness was in fact much lower than the value which it was thought had been achieved, due to an accumulation of flexibility in the circuit of small parts which alone gave only small deflections, but in total gave considerable deflection of the tailplane in rotation.

Although a torsional stiffness test had previously been done on the tailplane it was aimed at checking torsional, and not rotational stiffness.

On looking back over what has been written so far, we can now see how serious was the problem of flutter for the early transonic aircraft. In one case, the Handley-Page 88, the pilot had been killed; in two cases, the Boulton Paul Delta and the Folland Gnat, the pilots had to abandon the aircraft although, fortunately, both survived. In the case of the Javelin, some pieces of structure had broken away and the pilot survived a crash-landing. In the cases of the Supermarine 508, the Swift, and the Hunter, no major structure was fractured. Flutter was clearly not just an academic exercise and structural engineers were in the front line of the 'sound barrier' battle.

It was intended to build more advanced supersonic models of the Gnat with thinner wings and reheat, but these, like so many other projects, were abandoned when the contraction of the British Aircraft Industry began.

One other feature of high performance aircraft design had become critical in the 1950s and this concerned equipment, in particular electrical and electronic equipment. Early aircraft systems had tended to be mechanical, i.e., hydraulic or pneumatic, and were of fairly substantial build. They were not subjected to the extremes of temperature and pressure later to be endured by high flying, jet-propelled aeroplanes and were fairly immune to the ravages of vibration. For these reasons they tended to be treated as something of secondary importance.

However, vibration began to become a serious problem as miniature electronic components were introduced having nothing like the robust construction of mechanical systems. More extensive vibration surveys of aircraft structures were then needed as equipment failures tended to occur with annoying frequency. Some failures were merely time wasting, others dangerous.

For some years ground tests in climatic chambers had helped to solve temperature and pressure problems before expensive test flying took place, but it was becoming clear that much more comprehensive environmental test facilities were going to be needed, particularly to guard

Photograph 35. The author holding a model Supermarine Swift during a lecture to the Yorkshire Branch of the Institution of Mechanical Engineers in Sheffield (1954). (Sheffield Newspapers Limited)

against damage by vibration. The extreme reliability of any modern aircraft in fact owes much to the increased use of environmental testing which has now become an important technology.

(AUTHOR'S NOTE: On Saturday, 6 February 1954, I gave a lecture to the Yorkshire Branch of the Institution of Mechanical Engineers (Graduates Section) at Sheffield College of Technology. The title was 'Flight Testing of Aircraft', and the intense interest in this subject at that time caused the Press to attend. Almost as an afterthought, I mentioned that flying hours were being lost by equipment failure and that more ground test (i.e., environmental) facilities were required. This of course was news and in the *Sheffield Telegraph* of Monday, 8 February 1954, there was a photograph of myself (Photograph 35) with the caption 'Expert wants more jet ground tests'. I was somewhat embarrassed. Being about the most junior member of Supermarine's Flight Test section at the time, I did not consider myself by any means an expert. The reporter, of course, was simply doing his job but my conscience was eased when, that same week, no less a person than Sir Roy Fedden, by then a consultant to the Dowty Group, pleaded the same cause in a well-known journal.

In the end honour was satisfied when the Branch awarded me the Graduates lecture prize for that year.)

Sufficient has been said in this chapter, it is hoped, to convey the atmosphere of exploration which surrounded British aircraft research and production in the 1950s. Previously, aircraft design had been concerned with making small advances in familiar territory. When Mach number became more significant than pure speed, attention had to be focused on the complete flight environment rather than on a specific aircraft design. It is not surprising, therefore, that aircraft testing methods changed radically to meet the new needs. The Aeroplane and Armament Experimental Establishment at Boscombe Down was prominent in formulating suitable test methods and maintaining Britain's widely envied place in this field.

In defining the objectives of Boscombe Down in the new era, a former Superintendent of Performance had this to say:

> In contrast to previously, we now aim to do all we can to ensure a satisfactory aircraft reaches the Service at the planned date; previously the Establishment remained aloof and its function was to assess the aircraft at the eleventh hour and pronounce on its goodness. Our whole outlook and policy is now orientated, therefore, to do what we can to avoid eleventh hour crises, as with the expense and complications of modern aircraft it is a National Catastrophe if the aircraft fails to come up to expectations. Previously, such a situation was safeguarded by ordering from, say, two firms, but this is no longer practicable economics.

After the days of the Swift, Hunter, and their contemporaries, some dramatic military aircraft cancellations directed the attention of the general public away from technical achievement to the more pressing problems of aircraft economics, and some of the thrill went out of the job, but next we recall the years which saw the revival of a British supersonic flight programme and whose results, at the time of writing, have reached a climax in Concorde.

6

PRIDE AFTER PREJUDICE

On 16 March 1950, Mr Emmanuel Shinwell, then Minister of Defence, presented the Defence Estimates in the House of Commons. In the process he announced the start of work on aircraft capable of level flight supersonic speed, a welcome disclosure coming at a time when Britain's aeronautical reputation was none too high.

For security reasons it could not then be revealed that design studies of these aircraft had commenced two years earlier, but as we learned in Chapter 3, British supersonic policy was long term and first included a thorough exploration of the transonic region with various experimental aircraft. We shall now therefore look at the purely supersonic aircraft programme which had its origins in a committee formed at the RAE Farnborough in 1948 and known as The Advanced Fighter Project Group. It held numerous meetings between 1 March and 31 August of that year and finally issued a report in November 1948.

The terms of reference of this Group, whose Chairman was the late Sir Morien Morgan (then Mr Morgan), were:

1. Ensuring that the fullest use was being made of existing knowledge.
2. Making recommendations for future work on the specific problems thrown up by advanced fighters.

The Group report had this to say on the policy aspects:

If we had unlimited time the obvious way . . . would be to tackle the problem slowly but surely, starting off with tunnel and small free flight models and working up to the smallest piloted experimental aircraft that we can conceive for supersonic speeds. By this means we would amass the requisite information on lift, drag, stability, and control, and could proceed to the design of the operational machine with some measure of confidence – at least on the aerodynamic side.

It would, however, inevitably be a lengthy process. At present the timescale must obviously be a dominating factor in military aircraft development. In view of this we would like to suggest, in all seriousness, that we take a short cut by proceeding forthwith with the design of a fully operational supersonic fighter. . . .

From a purely technical standpoint an important statement was made which ran contrary to some opinions of the time:

We would stress that we dismiss completely any conception of an aircraft which must accelerate rapidly through the transonic region in order to be safe; in our view an operational military aircraft must be fully under control when flown steadily at any speed between the low speed stall and its top operational speed.

A level flight Mach number of 1·4 was envisaged although ultimately this was greatly exceeded, and, to enable work to start on the aircraft, a specification ER103 was issued. The responsibility for satisfying this need then fell not on the traditional builders of high-speed aircraft but on two firms, English Electric Aviation Limited, and the Fairey Aviation Co. Limited, neither of whom had previously produced manned aircraft with anything like the performance then being planned. This was probably an advantage. A fresh look at the problems of supersonic flight was badly needed, so when English Electric Aviation Limited produced their P1 prototype, followed shortly by the Fairey Aviation Company's FD2, two things were clear. First, both firms had departed radically, and perhaps not surprisingly, from previous design layouts. Second, in aiming at a common goal, they had adopted different philosophies which represented yet another divergence of opinion on how best to exist in the supersonic atmosphere.

The P1 possessed wings with a high degree of sweepback (60 degrees) and also a tailplane in the conventional position at the rear of the fuselage. In contrast the FD2 was a delta configuration. Both aircraft are shown in Photographs 36a and b.

Early transonic flight testing had shown, as we have read, that poorly damped oscillations of a whole aircraft in all planes could occur, particularly with tailless designs such as the deH.108, and even on those with tailplanes. In an RAE Technical Memo the question was asked, 'Is a tail necessary?', and in reply the following was written.

It seems best to leave this question open to discussion with the following remarks:

(a) It may be wise to get longitudinal *control* from a tail rather than the overburdened wing tip.

(b) It may be necessary to have a tail as a provider of longitudinal *damping*.

Photograph 36a. Fairey Delta FD2. This aircraft, flown by Peter Twiss, captured the world's air speed record on 10 March 1956, at an average speed of 1132 miles/h.
(Fairey Aviation Limited)

Photograph 36b. P1 Lightning. The aircraft shown here is one of the final variants with decreased sweep on outboard wing and enlarged fuel tank under the fuselage.
(British Aerospace)

(c) It is not easy to find a position for the tail behind low aspect ratio wings in which it is an efficient source of *static stability* at subsonic speeds and thus its presence may accentuate the inevitable increase in stability at supersonic speeds.

(d) The consensus of pilots opinion is that a tail is worth having.

It needs little imagination to detect in these words the prejudice against tailless aircraft, but this did not necessarily extend to the delta which could be fitted with a horizontal tail surface if necessary, the Javelin being an example.

It will be of interest now to quote from a joint lecture given to the Royal Aeronautical Society on 14 February 1957 by Mr R. L. Lickley, then Technical Director and Chief Engineer of the Fairey Aviation Co. Limited, and Mr Peter Twiss, a Test Pilot of the same Company. The lecturers described the development of the FD2 from many aspects and in speaking of the reasons why a delta plan form was adopted said among other things:

> The 60° delta . . . provided adequate damping in pitch which, combined with the power of large trailing edge control surfaces made the need for a tailplane superfluous. This decision was, however, not arrived at without considerable argument, but we know of very few high speed aeroplanes that have not at some time suffered from tail buffeting or other tailplane problems, and it has always seemed to us that perhaps the best way of avoiding them is not to have a tailplane at all.

The emphasis here was on structural and operational considerations. Earlier suggestions for tailless supersonic aircraft had of course originated from the obsession for drag reduction but as so little was still known of this aspect the maximum speeds of both the P1 and FD2 were difficult to predict and were eventually better than expected. Many cases of tail buffeting were of course cured by very simple changes, e.g. the Hunter, but at the start of the FD2 design the cures were not so generally recognized due to lack of experience.

Speaking in a discussion which followed the FD2 lecture, Mr F. W. Page (now Sir Frederick Page), then Chief Engineer of English Electric Aviation, commented on the Fairey Aviation philosophy as follows:

> If instead of using the trailing edge of the delta for elevators, a small notch-shaped portion aft was removed and used as an all moving pitch control . . . it helped the problem considerably. It also appreciably improved the damping of the short period pitching motion and permitted the use of flaps which eased the

152

approach and landing problem. Provided that this surface was positioned correctly in relation to the downwash pattern, in the case of high swept wings that was usually below the wing plane of course, he did not think the difficulties mentioned by Mr Lickley need really be experienced.

Here then were two quite opposite opinions expressed by engineers eminent in their own field and each charged with developing for the country a worthy supersonic research aircraft. But variety is the spice of life and neither the Fairey team nor their counterparts at English Electric had much concrete research evidence to back up their opinions, which can be compared with the RAE remarks quoted earlier.

Some aircraft layouts suggested in the Advanced Fighter Project Group report in fact all showed tailplanes mounted high on the fin, and a quite severe difference of opinion between the RAE and the English Electric designers arose on the positioning of this item, but the firm's low mounted P1 design was ultimately accepted and proved successful. It is perhaps worth noting, however, that both positions were subsequently used with success on other designs.

On the overall design problems, the conclusion to the Project Group report tried to put everything in the right perspective by saying:

> . . . perhaps the aerodynamic difficulties of transonic flight have been given too much emphasis . . . structural efficiency is equally important and, apart from such obvious problems as flutter and distortion, the success of piloted supersonic flight will depend critically on weight economy.

(These words were to be of even more significance when it came to civil supersonic transport design.)

An earlier comment in the report had said:

> . . . a first class structural design team from the Industry should be asked to proceed now with the design of an operational supersonic fighter . . . and that if the initial detailed work and weight estimation indicated that the calculations . . . were sound, several prototypes should be built.

The P1 and FD2 became these prototypes but ultimately followed different development patterns, the former evolving into an operational fighter now known in the Royal Air Force as the Lightning, the latter remaining as a pure research vehicle of which only two were built. Plans were, however, made to produce a fighter version of the FD2 (Fig. 13) and although this never materialized, the French firm of Dassault took up the delta idea with their highly successful Mirage, whose variants have sold,

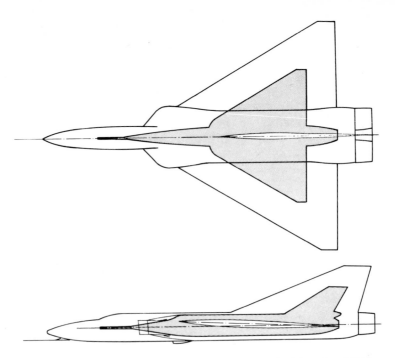

Figure 13. Plan and elevation of proposed Fairey supersonic delta winged Fighter aircraft. Superimposed (shaded) is the smaller record-breaking Fairey FD2 experimental aircraft.

and are still selling, throughout the world. Both the P1 and FD2 first flew in 1954 and for some time were the only British aircraft capable of level flight speeds greatly in excess of sound. Three others, the Saunders-Roe SR.53 mixed powerplant experimental fighter, the Bristol 188 research aircraft, and the British Aircraft Corporation's Tactical, Strike, Reconnaissance Bomber TSR.2, also possessed this capability but did very little flying and are now extinct, being remembered primarily for the circumstances of their cancellations.

Thus, for over a decade the British relied for piloted supersonic flight research on two designs conceived around 1950, and some were surprised that with this limited background they became involved in producing the world's first operational supersonic airliner. Technically the secret probably lay in the correct use of aimed research as opposed to mere data collecting with photogenic aircraft of doubtful potential, although certain economic factors should perhaps have been more deeply considered.

From the technical viewpoint, some forthright views were expressed during the Second International Congress in the Aeronautical Sciences at Zürich in 1960 by the late Dr Dietrich Küchemann, one-time Head of Aerodynamics Department at the RAE Farnborough. Speaking of the influence exerted on supersonic and other modes of flight by the complete family of aircraft designed during the first forty years of aviation, he included these remarks:

> Indeed so successful was this family of aircraft that many of its features have come to be regarded as fundamental to any aircraft whether supersonic, hypersonic or of the vertical take-off type, and when jet engines made supersonic flight possible it was assumed as a matter of course that a volume-providing non-lifting fuselage would have to be attached to a separate thin wing to do the lifting, with engines for propulsion. . . . As a consequence we had to live with what has been described as 'lousy flows'.
>
> We believe that this development was mistaken and propose, therefore, to start again and investigate whether a procedure similar to that just explained but with different initial assumptions may lead us to more natural and more efficient solutions for flight at supersonic speeds.

It is interesting to compare this proposal with the views of a great British engineer, I. K. Brunel, some one hundred years previously. Having examined the detail design of his iron ship *The Great Eastern*, he found that unnecessary material was being used due to the persistence of wooden ship techniques, and he stated:

> All this misconstruction I forbid and the consequence is that every part had to be considered and designed as if an iron ship had never been built before; indeed I believe we should get on much quicker if we had no previous habits and prejudices on the subject.

Both the P1 and FD2 could, in their original forms, be regarded as advanced types of traditional aircraft. They were, however, considerably modified over the years and can be counted among the vanguard of future supersonic designs. Let us see what was learned from them – we shall start with the Fairey FD2.

Following work on the FD1 mentioned in Chapter 3, Fairey was asked to submit proposals for a supersonic research aircraft preferably with a single engine both from supply and simplicity considerations. By December 1949, the intended design had crystallized, the final aircraft bearing a close resemblance to the original proposals.

Little information on delta layouts from either ground or flight tests was available to Fairey's designers and the ultimate success of the FD2 was almost certainly due to an uncompromising attitude to the requirement.

The design aim of the FD2, as expressed by Mr R. L. Lickley, was as follows:

> The major target and guiding principle in the whole design period was to get an aeroplane of minimum weight with the smallest frontal and surface areas while still remaining a straightforward aeroplane to handle in the air and on the ground, and yet at the same time large enough to house the RA.5 engine and sufficient fuel to enable worthwhile flights to be made.

Minimum weight and size is of course a general requirement but overemphasis on any one aspect could have been the death-knell of the FD2. Tradition was permitted little scope. To get the small frontal area, a maximum clearance of less than six inches was allowed between the engine and fuselage skin – the wing had to be thin so Fairey went for a 4 per cent thickness/chord ratio – at the time the lowest ever flown. Tailplanes had, on many designs, been troublesome so the delta layout was chosen. Power controls were essential and Fairey not only used their own but decided to fit a fully duplicated system without manual reversion, the first British aircraft to be so equipped. The innovation most obvious, however, was a drooping nose to improve the pilot's view for landing, although in the case of the FD2 this did not stem entirely from the extremely nose-high landing attitude made necessary by the lack of flaps. There was a special need to incorporate a low windscreen to reduce the drag due to shock waves and this of course restricted the view ahead more than usual. Once having clarified this requirement, Fairey were not deterred, however, by the engineering needed to droop the nose. The decision to use this system may in fact have been the most important single factor contributing to the ultimate success of the aircraft and this doubtless stemmed from their experience with folding wings on naval aircraft.

A Rolls-Royce Avon RA.5 engine, with reheat, supplied the thrust to propel the FD2 at whatever speed might be attained. In a structure so finely tailored a major problem was the accommodation of fuel. There was, as we have seen earlier, little point in designing for high performance if fuel shortage might terminate a flight before the maximum desired speed could be obtained. The fuel tanks were thus designed as an integral part of the wing.

Two models of the FD2 were built (Serial Nos. WG 774 and WG 777), the first, WG 774, making its first flight on 6 October 1954, at Boscombe Down. The contract to build these two aircraft was placed in October 1950, but serious design work could not be started at Fairey until mid-1952. This delay arose out of the 'super-priority' needs of another Fairey aircraft, the Gannet, which was being prepared for Naval service. Even wind-tunnel data was almost non-existent as the available tunnel capacity had to be devoted almost entirely to developing new military machines.

From the purely aerodynamic standpoint the FD2 was simply given the small changes of external contour which for some years had been known to yield advantages in the transonic and supersonic régimes, at least in the search for drag reduction.

In three other areas of design, in particular, there was less certainty. Knowledge of flutter at high Mach numbers was, as we have seen, very limited, and even irreversible powered controls could not guarantee freedom from this serious condition, particularly with very thin wings. Autostabilizers were not fitted and, although such devices were not essential on the FD2, other high-speed aircraft had either displayed a real need for them or at least had benefited from their presence. Fitting autostabilizers was not just a design problem. Considerable flight testing was needed in order to assess the consequences of failure and this took time. Finally, the behaviour of the engine and air intake system was a very unknown quantity. No experience was available of operating turbine-powered aircraft over the speed range envisaged for the FD2 and the fitting of reheat added to the uncertainty. If any of the items just mentioned had introduced unduly difficult or even dangerous charac-teristics, the FD2 might have had more limited success or might, at best, have taken longer to achieve the test programmes. As it was the British possessed, in this aircraft, a most valuable research tool whose usefulness continued for nearly two decades.

The début of the FD2 was strangely quiet, largely for security reasons. Photographs and vague details of the aircraft were generally released, but previous disappointments had so reduced people's confidence in British ability to be a major force in supersonic affairs that few could imagine that the FD2 would improve matters. A forced landing on the fourteenth flight of WG 774 in mid-November 1954, also did nothing to promote its image. But following extensive repair and modifications, flying recommenced in June 1955. Initial trials of the aerodynamic and structural properties continued, with emphasis being placed on flutter investigation and handling characteristics. Speed was increased in small stages, and on 28 October 1955, the first supersonic flight occurred. Reheat was not then cleared for use but without it the power was sufficient to achieve a Mach number of 1·1 in level flight. The passage through the transonic region was without incident, as indeed was the later flying at the much higher Mach numbers which finally proved possible, and compared with the early assault on the sound barrier with more conventional machines, the smoothness of it all was unbelievable.

Then came the day when reheat was first operated and an exciting prospect immediately opened up. Such speeds were achieved that the existing world record of 822 miles/h, held by an American, Colonel Haynes, flying an F100 Super Sabre, could obviously be exceeded handsomely by the FD2. Not only that but some possibility existed of pushing the record speed beyond 1000 miles/h for the first time. This additional temptation strongly attracted Fairey towards a record attempt. One major doubt, however, inevitably entered into the deliberations of those responsible for any decision to go ahead. Were the Americans currently capable of beating the FD2, and if they learned of the attempt would they once more walk off with a coveted prize? As it happened there was no need to worry; but once it had been decided to arrange for record runs the utmost secrecy surrounded the preparations.

Operation was to be from Boscombe Down to fly over a south coast speed course between Chichester and Ford at the high altitudes now permitted by international agreement. The performance attained by contenders had become such that to make the necessary runs just above ground-level was no longer possible. Aircraft structures would not withstand the loads produced by moving at maximum speed through the dense low altitude atmospheres and the massive fuel consumption of jet engines at such heights would not in any case allow the necessary flight time.

There was therefore no alternative but to consider a high-altitude course, and in the case of the FD2 this meant about 38 000 ft. Two main problems then arose, one concerning flying accuracy and the other the ability to measure the record speed by ground-based devices.

Fair play demanded a substantially straight and level flight path. To achieve this seven miles above the earth, with no fixed object available on which to line up, made reliance on the altimeter absolute. Now we saw in

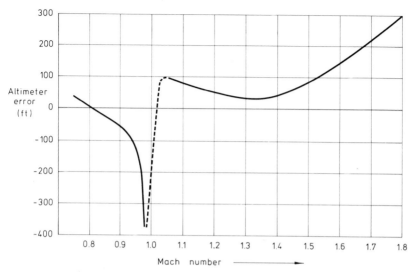

Figure 14. Fairey Delta 2. Effect of Mach number on altimeter reading.

Chapter 2 that large altimeter errors could occur in the transonic region and these could change rapidly with a change of Mach number. Figure 14 shows the FD2 altimeter correction for Mach numbers from 0·75 to 1·8. The sudden change shown around M = 1, then common to all aircraft, was caused by shock wave movement across the pressure head from which both speed and height readings were derived. How did this affect the speed record flight recording?

Suppose the aircraft accelerated in such a fashion that the altimeter reading was held constant at 38 000 ft. Table 7 shows what the true height would then be at various stages during an accelerated run.

Table 7

Mach number	True height (ft)
0·8	38 000
0·98	38 350
1·05	37 900
1·3	37 960
1·6	37 850
1·8	37 700

159

In this case a maximum height change of 650 ft actually occurs between Mach numbers of 0·98 and 1·8. For the speed-course runs the rules demanded a height separation not greater than 328 ft (100 m) between the entry point of each run. Careful allowance had therefore to be made for changes of altimeter error with Mach number, but first the errors themselves had to be measured accurately. This was done by flying past a specially calibrated Venom aircraft, which formed part of the comprehensive flight test facilities always available at Boscombe Down.

To fly level for the record attempt the pilot thus had to fly the aircraft so that the altimeter reading actually changed due to the errors that changed with speed. To appreciate the consequence of even the slightest departure from the ideal attitude, imagine a deviation of one degree nose up or nose down occurring at a Mach number of 1·7. In twenty seconds the height would then change by 340 ft. This problem is in fact now of major importance for the flight planning of supersonic airliners when height separation in airways is critical.

After all had been done to ensure that the FD2 had a sporting chance of flying sufficiently level to qualify for a record submission there still remained the great difficulty of measuring the result and guiding the pilot accurately over the speed course. This was, however, a ground-based operation and is not of primary concern to this book but those concerned deserve an honourable mention.

By the beginning of March 1956 all was ready for Fairey's sleek aeroplane and its pilot Peter Twiss to attack a record which for some time had been an American monopoly. On the tenth of that month, the weather was suitable for measuring record runs and several problems encountered in earlier attempts had been solved. A short flight of twenty-three minutes completed the proceedings. After shutting down the engine at the finish, Twiss had only about 6 per cent of usable fuel left – a tribute to the careful flight planning and a measure of the small margin available for error.

When final calculations were complete, the dual aim of breaking the speed record and exceeding 1000 miles/h had, to the great gratification of all, been realized, with a figure of 1132·2 miles/h, and this record stood for two years.

The news, when it broke, astonished everybody and was received almost with disbelief in America. Britain had for so long been lagging in the supersonic race and the Grand Slam perpetrated by the FD2 seemed utterly against the run of play. Strangely, although the country generally

160

rejoiced in the deeds of the FD2, the participation in record contests was regarded in some quarters as a diversion from badly needed research work. This view was not shared by the late Mr S. Scott Hall, one-time Air Ministry Scientific adviser, who commented:

The capture of the record gave the British Aircraft Industry a tremendous uplift.

Americans concerned with high speed aircraft development, no matter what type of wing they favoured, swept wing, straight wing, or delta wing, appeared to be equally surprised at the performance achieved.

So ended a twilight phase in British aeronautical progress. After the speed record was ratified the Fairey FD2 went, as planned, to the RAE Bedford. A comprehensive flight research programme then occupied the next five years after which the first of the type, WG 774, was sent to the then British Aircraft Corporation factory at Filton, near Bristol, to be modified in support of the Concorde programme. This involved about two years work and in its new form (see frontispiece) it resumed flying on 1 May 1964.

Success of course tends to emphasize the high point of achievement and for the FD2 this meant the speed record. In some ways this was unfortunate as it overshadowed the wider qualities of this excellent design, not only in terms of flying but also in terms of reliability. Up to 15 November 1956, the first FD2 had made 243 flights. Taking out the repair period of nine months following the forced landing, this works out at just under four flights per week. Not many, maybe, by modern airliner standards but good when each flight had to be carefully analysed before the next could take place. Of these 243 flights, 167 were supersonic, sometimes low down where the more dense air treats the structure severely. During a period of intensive flying at Cazaux, near Bordeaux in France, the FD2 made no less than 52 flights in one month, averaging about two per day, and on three occasions achieved five per day. It had gone there to perform low-altitude supersonic flying on account of the favourable weather conditions, the lowest supersonic flight being made at 3000 ft ($M=1.04$). This was a splendid achievement but the equipment failures and structural damage typically caused by buffeting on other transonic aircraft were largely absent on the FD2. For one thing it didn't buffet and in the words of a firm's report:

Transonic behaviour has confirmed the theoretical estimates and wind tunnel tests which suggested that the 60° delta planform gives the smoothest transition

161

from subsonic to supersonic flight. In our flying we have found the behaviour in the range $M=0.9$ to $M=1.1$ to be extremely smooth, the pilot noticing only a change of trim at $M=0.96$. . . .

The report went on to say that the Fairey powered flying controls had worked well. Several well-known designers from other firms subsequently paid tribute to the excellence of the FD2 engineering design which had contributed to the continuity of flying. It is interesting to reflect that the pioneer aviators, the Wright Brothers, had stressed the importance of a high intensity of flying if anything worthwhile was to be learned and had pointed out how little airborne time had been accumulated during early gliding experiments.

(AUTHOR'S NOTE: I remember occasions during the early days of supersonic testing when hardly a flight took place without some sort of failure. Two flights per week was a sadly common occurrence. One Boscombe Down test pilot was moved to write in a report that a certain notoriously unserviceable type of aircraft, '. . . would be better employed as a target than as a bomber'.)

Stability and control, performance, and engine behaviour naturally formed a major part of the work allotted to the FD2 programme. To assist in the interpretation of stability tests, considerable effort was devoted to the study of flow patterns and pressures around the wing – a task which it will be remembered formed a primary part of the deH.108 testing in 1948. This particular section of the investigation has in fact forged a link between the traditional aerodynamics, where air is expected to follow the aircraft contours, and the later concept of separated flow by which the lift necessary for landing a supersonic aircraft can be obtained without moving large sections of wing such as flaps.

Whatever may be said, however, of the aerodynamic design of the FD2 and P1 and their ability to be flown by experienced test pilots, operational versions still had to be suitable for piloting by average Royal Air Force pilots in weather conditions dictated by an enemy rather than by choice. As it happened, this concerned only the P1 and its descendants where 60 degrees of sweepback raised problems of low-speed flying. In particular it had to be known whether any airflow separation would be orderly enough to permit the use of conventional flying techniques for landing. A high landing speed seemed inevitable but a comprehensive flight test programme was planned to reduce the difficulties as far as possible and once again the scale model technique was used to great advantage. Short Bros. and Harland were brought into the act and were awarded a contract to build a low-powered low-speed research aircraft to investigate flight characteristics of highly swept wings. In response they produced their SB5 which is shown in Photographs 37a and b. The resemblance between this and the P1 is very noticeable.

Some background to the SB5 work is expressed in an RAE Technical Report from which the following extracts are taken:

The continual increase in speed of aircraft has led to wing planforms with increasing sweepback and lower aspect ratios. These particular planform characteristics have been adopted largely from performance considerations. It is, of course, necessary that aircraft be controllable throughout their operating speed range and the fact that the wing design has been determined in the first instance by high speed requirements might be expected to cause problems in the low speed régime of take-off and landing. . . .

. . . At the time of the initial conception of the Short SB5 research aircraft (1949) it was recognized that the trend towards higher angles of sweepback was likely to continue and this was emphasized by the existence of a design for an operational fighter aircraft, the English Electric P1 (Lightning) which was to have a sweepback of 60°. There was then no flight experience with wings of this amount of sweepback. The SB5 was designed to allow a gradual approach to this configuration, flying initially with 50° sweepback before conversion to 60° when it would resemble, aerodynamically, a seven-eighths scale model of the Lightning. To increase its usefulness as a research vehicle the aircraft was capable of further modification to operate with 69° of wing sweepback.

A Rolls-Royce Derwent jet engine provided the power for the SB5, and a facility for fitting lead ballast in the nose and under the wings enabled the effects of centre of gravity movement and varying configurations to be studied.

Making its first flight in December 1952, almost two years before the P1, the SB5 operated initially from Boscombe Down. It was transferred to RAE Farnborough in June 1954, and to RAE Bedford in August 1956, where testing with 60 degree sweep continued until April 1958.

As the basic wing planform and cross-section themselves might have been inadequate for some modes of flight, provision was made for investigating the effects of several combinations of wing leading edge contour, leading edge and trailing edge flap, and tailplane vertical location.

After about six months of flying with 50 degree wing sweepback the

Photograph 37a. Short SB5 research aircraft with tailplane as originally fitted on top of fin.
(Short Bros. and Harland)

Photograph 37b. Short SB5 with tailplane fitted low on fuselage to simulate configuration of Lightning Fighter. Compare this aircraft with Lightning shown in Photograph 36b.
(Short Bros. and Harland)

sweep angle was increased to 60 degrees and flying with this planform commenced in July 1953. At this time a drooped wing leading edge was fitted and the tailplane had been fixed low on the fuselage to resemble the P1 configuration. A wing leading edge flap was also operative and the wing leading edge droop retained. The initial aim was to perform enough flying to give confidence in the P1 layout before a full-size aircraft made its first flight.

In February 1954, the drooped wing leading edge was removed and from that moment the SB5 simulated aerodynamically the basic layout of a prototype P1. It was not lacking in vices. In particular, an unpleasant wing drop could occur at moderate angles of incidence. A cure for this consisted of a leading edge spoiler but such a device was not favoured for the P1 and eventually it was found that a small notch cut in the leading edge prevented the wing drop equally effectively. Several other problems were also resolved with the SB5. Thus when the first P1 WG 760 (or P1A to use the exact designation) took off from Boscombe Down on its maiden flight on 4 August 1954, yet another British aircraft was launched on a successful career thanks in no small part to piloted model research.

A comparison between the P1 and designs suggested in the Advanced Fighter Project Group Report is perhaps of some interest at this stage. In 1948 the most powerful engine under development, which could have been suitable for a supersonic fighter, was the Bristol TE 1/46, eventually known as the Olympus, and with such powerplants it had been calculated that the aircraft required might weigh anything from 30 000 lb to 46 000 lb in the later forms.

The TE 1/46 originally appeared to be a logical choice for an engine and at least two or possibly three per aircraft were thought to be needed to overcome the predicted drag values. Eventually in the RAE report it was suggested that the two-engined layout with its saving in weight would be the best. This was a fortunate decision for, by the time serious design work started, the smaller Sapphire and Avon engines were giving, or gave promise of giving, enough thrust for the job.

Despite the advantages thus obtained, the concern for reducing drag was, however, such that an attempt was even made to eliminate the normal pilot's cockpit by fitting a prone (face down) pilot's position in the bottom of the air intake. Such a position also enabled the pilot to withstand greater 'g' forces, an important advantage in combat aircraft. Figure 15 shows how this would have looked and for comparison the same design with a

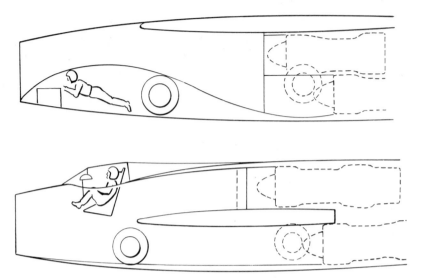

Figure 15. Alternative pilot accommodation in early proposals for first British supersonic Fighter aircraft. Upper view shows prone position once thought necessary to eliminate drag of cockpit canopy.

normal upright seating arrangement is shown together with a P1A front fuselage layout.

A prone cockpit was in fact fitted experimentally to a Meteor fighter and, although shown to be a practical proposition, was said, perhaps not surprisingly, to be inferior to the natural seating position. In the end a better understanding of supersonic aerodynamics enabled quite low drag canopies to be designed. In recent years, the development of automatic flying controls, requiring less physical effort by the pilot, has allowed cockpit seats on fighter aircraft to be less vertical but, in contrast to the earlier face down arrangement, they now recline more comfortably backwards.

Two P1A aircraft were ordered for flight trials and a third for static tests. Each flying prototype was powered by two Armstrong-Siddeley Sapphire engines, and on its third flight, exactly one week after first becoming airborne in August 1954, WG 760 exceeded the speed of sound. It was the first British aircraft capable of doing this in level flight and its unusual apearance not only attracted attention but commanded respect.

166

authorities lax in their supervision of fuel contamination – did it contain water, sand, or other foreign material? It was certainly beginning to look as if some common factor was involved in the Comet crashes, the similarity of the Elba and Naples tragedies being too obvious. In consequence Sir Arnold Hall, then Director of the RAE Farnborough, proposed that a comprehensive fatigue test of a complete Comet pressure cabin should be made. Previous tests had been confined to selected sections of the cabin, so something much more than a repeat of those tests was envisaged. The job was not easy and had originally been performed by pumping air into the test specimen, which, if it ruptured, could explode with the force of a small bomb. It was not unknown for test personnel to be injured even when housed in concrete shelters and there was always the chance that the disintegration could destroy evidence of the cause of failure. It was therefore decided, in the case of the Comet, to use a recently developed technique in which water pressure and not air was used to apply the repeated test cabin loads. The whole cabin was in fact completely immersed in a large water tank. The idea was that water, being incompressible, would produce only a mild explosion in the event of failure.

Such was the urgency of the job that by early June 1954, only two months after the Naples crash, a large water tank and its pumping equipment was ready to commence tests. Comet G-ALYU became the test specimen. This aircraft had already made 1230 pressurized flights, and after the equivalent of a further 1830 such flights in the test tank (making a total of 3060), the cabin structure unexpectedly failed, starting at the corner of a small radio aerial window on top of the fuselage.

Although examination of the Elba wreckage had not, at that stage, yielded any conclusive evidence to account for the crashes, the water tank tests pointed to a pressure cabin failure as being the most likely primary cause. A closer examination of the existing wreckage now tended to support this view and it was subsequently thought desirable to search a wider area of sea off Elba for vital portions of the structure of G-ALYP. This paid off handsomely. The piece of fuselage containing the initial failure around two windows was found (Photograph 42) as well as pieces of wing bearing paint marks which could only have been made by flying debris from the exploding pressure cabin. The official accident report has this to say about these findings:

> . . . they established that the cabin burst catastrophically in the neighbourhood of the front spar of the wing when the aircraft was flying substantially normally.

Photograph 42. Origin of Comet pressure cabin failure. The small radio aerial windows on top of the fuselage. Skin cracks around edges of windows can be seen. (Royal Aircraft Establishment – Crown Copyright)

By examination of the piece containing the . . . windows, and the adjacent pieces, it was established that it was here that the first fracture of the cabin structure occurred. . . .

Considering the evidence as a whole it was stated that:

. . . the highest stress in the skin, at the edge near the corner of the window . . . was probably over 40,000 lb per square inch . . . and that the general level of stress in the skin in these regions was significantly higher than had been previously believed.

. . . the fundamental cause of the failure of the cabin structure was that there existed around the corners of the windows and other cut-outs, a level of stress higher than is consistent with a long life of the cabin, bearing in mind the unavoidable existence of points, within the areas of generally high stress, at which it will be still further raised by relatively local influences. . . .

This was the real crux of the matter. If the structure loading had been of the believed level, the pressure cabin would have been safe, and the

180

gamble in producing the Comet would have succeeded. It was probably too much to expect that Britain could lead in both jet engine and jet airliner development at that time but the Comet lesson benefited aviation throughout the world and that was perhaps some small compensation for losing the aircraft and those who died.

The first major setback along the road to commercial supersonic flight was thus attributable not to the new look aerodynamics nor to the engines which had made it all possible, but to the old problem of structural failure. Considering the scale of the Comet disaster and the very nature of the earth's atmosphere, it is surprising that the concept of a 'height barrier' didn't emerge. Certainly some of the perils then lurking at high altitude rivalled those associated purely with high speed and Mach number. The effect of speed on the human imagination has, however, always been profound, so the height researchers plodded devotedly along their unglamorous way until the Comet gave them such unwelcome publicity.

Fortunately the Comet survived in concept, and although the earlier types flew again with strengthened structures, they did not re-enter regular passenger service. Later versions, however, powered by Rolls-Royce Avon engines, became available, and British Overseas Airways Corporation (BOAC) decided that, at least for a limited period, these could be used on North Atlantic crossings. As a result the first-ever transatlantic jet air service opened on 4 October 1958, when two Comet 4s simultaneously made the London–New York and New York–London run. This was a first-class publicity project, but larger machines were really required, and Britain was soon forced to purchase American Boeing 707s in the face of a storm of opposition from its aircraft industry, press, and any patriot capable of protesting. This caused a temporary retreat from the field of long-range jet transport, but Comets continued to give good service on European and Commonwealth routes and also served with the Royal Air Force. Some performed valuable research work on navigation, blind landing, and other duties. Finally, when Coastal Command required new aircraft, a redesigned Comet, renamed Nimrod (Photograph 43) and powered by Rolls-Royce Spey engines, was produced. This joined the Royal Air Force exactly twenty years after the original Comet first left the ground, and will be in service for many more years.

If the Comet disasters produced valuable results they were not the results of premeditated research, and other experiments were more

Photograph 43. Nimrod maritime reconnaissance aircraft. Developed from the Comet which it closely resembles. Rolls-Royce Spey engines fitted in place of the Avon which powered all but the early Comets.
(British Aerospace)

Photograph 44. The Avro Ashton. Nothing like supersonic but rendered great service investigating problems of flight at the high altitudes where jet bombers and transports were to operate.
(British Aerospace)

fortunate in their origins. Of these, mention should be made of a batch of aircraft which unobtrusively made considerable contributions to technical knowledge. The type concerned was also powered by four jet engines and known as the Avro Ashton (Photograph 44). Derived from an experimental jet-powered version of the early Tudor airliner, no less than six Ashtons were built for the Ministry of Supply. They undertook a wide variety of research into engine behaviour, cabin conditioning, electrical systems, and weapons, but were not capable of attaining high Mach numbers, a deficiency which meant that the prototypes of large transonic aircraft were still exploring the unknown. The first Ashton WB 940 first flew on 1 September 1950, and an outline of the overall work undertaken by this and other Ashtons is shown in Table 8.

Table 8

Serial number	First flew	Tasks performed
WB 940	1.9.50	High altitude jet engine research. Auto pilot tests
WB 941	2.8.51	Pressure cabin research Jet engine research (Avon, Conway, Sapphire)
WB 942	6.7.51	Research into radar bombing
WB 943	18.12.51	Electrical and instrument research. Engine research (Olympus, Orpheus)
WB 494	18.11.52	Visual bombing Engine de-icing (Sapphire)
WB 670	9.4.52	Bomb research Engine de-icing (Avon).

By the time the last Ashton had flown in November 1952, however, its designers, A. V. Roe & Company Limited, had built and flown the prototype of a very different aeroplane, the Vulcan. This was also a four-jet machine, a bomber of great potential, and the next part of this chapter describes how the Vulcan and its contemporaries wrought a great change in the British aviation scene.

In contrast to the struggle taking place for civil jet supremacy, the picture on the military side was more clear cut. When the Air Estimates were discussed in Parliament on 15 March 1949, Mr Arthur Henderson, then Secretary of State for Air, dealt at some length with long-term bomber production. He made it clear that Britain had, after World War II, deliberately avoided ordering heavy bombers based on existing and early type jet engines. Such aircraft would have had a limited value and life. Instead it had been decided to wait for the next generation of engines and use them in bombers of advanced concept, thereby obtaining the best of all worlds. In the meanwhile, a mixture of obsolete Lancaster, Lincoln, and American-made Washington aircraft at least kept Bomber Command airborne. As it happened there were only a few weeks to wait before the maiden flight, on 13 May 1949, of Britain's first jet bomber, the Canberra. Although this was only in the tactical class and could not carry the bulky atomic bombs of those days, it was nevertheless capable, in large numbers, of causing severe destruction with conventional bombs, and few would have thought that thirty years later it would still be in service and capable of delivering the smaller atomic weapons then available.

From the 1949 Air Estimates, it was apparent that the design of a new heavy bomber fleet was actually under way, although a certain amount of impatience was expressed by His Majesty's Opposition at the timescales involved. Two specifications of 1946 vintage were being actioned, B14/46 and B35/46. To the former was designed and built by Short Brothers and Harland of Belfast, Britain's first four-engined jet heavy bomber, the Sperrin. This machine displayed a performance much superior to the latter-day piston-engined bombers but it was not so advanced as the types proposed in the later specification. After two prototypes had been built they were consequently diverted to a research role.

The second bomber specification quoted, B35/46, gave birth to a trio of aircraft probably as effective as any possessed in peacetime by the Royal Air Force. To become known popularly as the V-bombers from their names of Valiant, Vulcan, and Victor, these three were designed by Vickers-Armstrongs, A. V. Roe, and Handley-Page, respectively. All were powered by four engines and for a significant period were the only large aircraft possessed by Britain having a high subsonic speed capability. The first flight dates of the first of each type were:

Valiant   18 May 1951
Vulcan   30 August 1952
Victor   24 December 1952

and illustrations of each can be seen in Photographs 45a–c.

It has been said that this ordering of three separate aircraft was economically and logistically unwise but this assumes some certain knowledge of their capabilities and perhaps ignores the great uncertainties of the early transonic era. The Valiant design actually fell slightly short of the full requirements of specification B35/46, but being the more conventional of the three it appeared capable of flying before its companions. As an insurance against the failure of either the Vulcan or Victor, a new specification was therefore written, B9/48, and it was to this that the Valiant was expected to conform.

The difficulties of intercepting such fast bombers flying at extreme altitudes were generally acknowledged and we mentioned something of this problem in Chapter 5. The chance of Britain remaining a major nation thus depended to a large extent on controlling a home-built nuclear bomber fleet, and the V-bombers were important if only for this reason. But they also gave to Britain the status of being the only country outside the USA and USSR to have designed, built, and flown a large transonic jet aircraft, an advantage with civil as well as military potential. Whereas the Comet had pioneered high-altitude flying in the 40 000 ft region, the V-bombers advanced the frontiers of speed and Mach number for aircraft of such size. Their historical significance thus extends much beyond their role purely as bombers, so let us see how they originated and developed.

In the same way that British supersonic fighters were first studied by a special project group, so an organization known as the Advanced Bomber Project Group was formed within the RAE Farnborough. Also chaired by the late Sir Morien Morgan, this group assembled on 25 November 1947, and held a total of four meetings, the last being on 26 January 1948.

A requirement from the Air Staff called for bombers capable of carrying 10 000 lb of bombs at 500 knots over ranges of 3350–4350 nautical miles at a height of 50 000 ft. A cruising Mach number of 0·87 was envisaged. It was realized from the outset that the task was enormous and in the group report it was said in the introduction:

The design, construction and development of these advanced bombers will be a fairly lengthy business and – in order to meet a tight time limit for the date at which fully operational squadrons must be equipped with such machines – decisions of far reaching importance must be made forthwith. Numerous approaches to the design problem are apparent at this stage and mistakes made now in the basic conceptions may well prove impossible to rectify later. While some relief may be afforded by spreading the risk – selecting several designs, for example, a low aspect ratio delta shape, a high aspect ratio swept wing, and

Photograph 45a. Vickers Valiant. The first of the V-Bombers. Valiants were withdrawn from Royal Air Force service in 1965.
(British Aerospace)

Photograph 45b. Handley-Page Victor. The crescent wing can be seen in this view of a Victor tanker refuelling Lightning Fighters. Compare with wing of Handley-Page HP.88 (Photograph 23).
(British Aerospace)

Photograph 45c. Avro Vulcan. The only one of the V-Bombers still serving in the original bomber role. This particular aircraft is shown carrying an experimental 'Olympus' engine for research in connection with Concorde.
(British Aerospace)

something in between – it is vitally important that the designs chosen for spreading the risk should form some sort of logical pattern which, on the basis of existing knowledge, gives the best chance of one at least of the chosen designs meeting the exacting requirements.

It was stated very early in the report that a practicable advanced bomber could not be produced by relying solely on thin straight wings and that sweepback would have to be used. In this connection it is interesting to read how the results of the de Havilland 108 flying were also used to assist the bomber programme.

A preliminary flight-tunnel comparison of the swept tail-less deH.108 has revealed appreciably less drag at high Mach number in flight than that indicated by the high speed tunnel tests.

When all the deliberations were complete it was recommended that three types of aircraft should be built.

Firstly a tailed aircraft of aspect ratio between 5 and 6 and with 45° of sweepback.

Secondly a tail-less delta aircraft of aspect ratio 3. . . . Thirdly, we would suggest a design intermediate between the above two extremes – namely a tailed aircraft of aspect ratio 4 and with only 35° sweepback, the smaller sweepback being compensated by thinner wings. . . .

These proposals eventually gave rise to the Victor, Vulcan, and Valiant, respectively, and in outlining a course of action it was emphasized that there was a need for:

Building up experience on the problems of operating at extreme altitudes, when suitable pressurised equipment is available.

and further:

A concerted effort by the Industry and the Establishments is needed here, since although we are busily engaged in designing for 50,000 feet, experience at such heights is almost non-existent. Quite apart from aerodynamic problems we have in mind the whole wide field – engine behaviour, pressurisation technique, navigational and instrumental problems, safety aspects, etc. . . .

But there was no guarantee that the proposed aircraft would be operationally effective even if they achieved immediately their specified speeds and heights. Only by gradual development could this ultimate goal be reached and of the many contributory factors probably none was more important than flying accuracy.

For many years it had been recognized that as aircraft performance increased so would the need for mechanisms to assist the human piloting function, and the two decades prior to the birth of the V-bombers had seen the introduction of what was known first as a 'Pilot's Assister' and subsequently as an automatic pilot. These devices were, however, intended solely for gentlemanly subsonic conditions, and when transonic flight with its disturbed aerodynamic situations had to be tamed, a more comprehensive and more sensitive range of automatic flying controls was required. An additional major element was thereby brought into the process of aircraft design and testing, but as far as the V-bombers were concerned it enabled them to make their most valuable single contribution to British aviation progress for, by developing the latest automatic flight control systems to suit their own needs, they provided a major stepping-stone not only to Concorde but also to other military, civil, and even Space applications. The events leading up to this desirable state are of direct interest to our story so we shall now describe how such a vital link with the future was forged.

Many readers may be surprised to learn that schemes were afoot for controlling flying machines automatically before even one of them had flown. The pioneers did not, of course, want to make their own job unnecessarily difficult but they did fear that in gusty wind conditions pilots would need mechanical assistance to maintain steady flight, and the first use envisaged for automatic controls was thus to achieve stability. There was, however, some reason to hope that artificial forms of control might not after all be needed, at least for this purpose, for in 1894 F. W. Lanchester conducted his classic experiments which formed a basis for all future aircraft stability and control design whether of natural or automatic origin. From a bedroom window in his home in Warwick, Lanchester launched his rubber powered model aircraft and observed systematically how the shape, weight, and area distribution of each model influenced the flight path following an atmospheric disturbance. He concluded that by suitable design it was possible to make a stable flying machine without the '. . . employment of any equilibrium mechanism or brain equivalent. . . .'

As we now know this prophecy proved correct and most of the early aircraft could be controlled sufficiently by human hand to enable the elements of flying to be learned, but if, from the ground, a full-size aircraft appeared to fly as smoothly as Lanchester's models, this did not mean that the pilot was having an easy time. One does not have to fly to realize that even a small disturbance can lower human efficiency enormously, so until manned flight took place, little could really be learned of a pilot's flying efficiency and his need for assistance. It helped of course that man's magnificent new toys were not expected to land like birds, delicately, on the branches of trees. When therefore a few of them inadvertently achieved this feat it was not regarded as advancing the state of the art.

An automatic flying control had to be designed around a device with the power and sensitivity to fly an aeroplane safely, if needs be for long periods, but until airborne experiments had shown how much power and sensitivity were needed the problem could only be considered in general terms. It was nevertheless almost certain that any immediate solution would be of a mechanical nature for electrical technology was not sufficiently advanced to be of help. There were two or three possible ways of achieving automatic flight, but one of them, the gyroscope, found most

189

favour particularly following the pioneer work of the American Elmer Sperry, whose name is linked with gyroscopes in the way Marconi is linked with radio.

But gyroscopes had been used in moving vehicles before the beginning of the twentieth century, to stabilize ships and to guide torpedoes, although in these cases weight was not critical. For aircraft use, weight was, of course, critical and it remained to be seen if the correspondingly small controlling forces of gyroscopes could be amplified sufficiently to move an aircraft control surface.

An early proposal to do this in England had been made in 1891 by Sir Hiram Maxim, an American by birth, who subsequently took British nationality. He constructed a monster steam-powered flying machine with the intention of fitting gyroscopic control, but this creation was unfortunately damaged and never flew, despite showing considerable lifting powers during tethered runs. A decade then elapsed until flying proved to be possible and the controls of individual aircraft could be extensively tested, but, if the general public were thrilled by the pioneer aviation scene, some of the technically minded were more reserved, and J. H. Ledeboer made the following comment on the possible limitations of human skill in the October 1911 edition of *Aeronautics* of which he was then editor:

It is necessary to make it clear once and for all that if the aeroplane is to make any real progress in the future, it is absolutely essential that . . . stability should be realised to a far greater extent that it yet has been. A certain element of personal control on the part of the pilot will always be required but this should be super-added to the natural stability always possessed by the machine, by virtue either of the disposition of its surfaces and weights or by a mechanical device working automatically under all conditions.

Time was to show that even the best of aeroplanes could in fact be improved by having an auto pilot, if only to prevent pilot fatigue, but with 'heavier-than-air' flight only eleven years old came World War I, and in 1917 plans for a pilotless guided bomb emerged from the Royal Aircraft Factory at Farnborough. To guide this weapon radio signals were transmitted from the ground but these merely caused the main flying controls to make crude movements; there was no question of independent monitoring by on-board machinery and the idea was not developed. But in 1920 interest in the pilotless aircraft was renewed for use both as a weapon and as a target for gunnery practice. A small machine equipped with a gyro-controlled rudder was therefore constructed for flight trials. Changes

190

in the flight path were initiated not by radio signals from the ground but by a timing switch within the aircraft itself and take-off was from a ramp over the side of a Royal Navy ship.

The first tests immediately produced some wild rolling manoeuvres which although appearing to indicate failure did nevertheless contain a hidden element of success, for it was found that the gyro itself was causing the trouble but not through any fault of its own. It was simply being affected by the climbing attitude of the aircraft, and when the reasons for this were understood it was realized that both the rudder and the elevator could be controlled simultaneously by a single gyroscope instead of each having a separate unit. This was the turning point in developing a simple reliable automatic pilot and real progress was then made. Six launches of the pilotless aircraft were made up to September 1924 with increasing success, and on the seventh launch, on the twenty-fourth of that month, radio control gear was introduced for the first time.

In parallel with the pilotless aircraft tests, a World War I Bristol Fighter was used to observe at first hand the effects of gyro controls, and in 1921 an aircraft of this type equipped with a gyro rudder was steered automatically in response to radio signals from the ground.

A comprehensive, systematic, picture of automatic flight requirements was thus built up, the success of which owed much to F. W. Meredith of the RAE, who subsequently became one of the foremost British authorities on practical auto pilots. At the same time, some of the earliest mathematical studies of automatic control effects were undertaken by S. B. Gates, who for many years specialized in stability and control work at the RAE Farnborough, and by 1925 British engineers had advanced probably as far as any towards a simple substitute for the human pilot, at least for steady flight.

It was in fact in 1925 that Meredith, in conjunction with P. A. Cooke, also of the RAE, started the design for an auto-pilot system that was to be used for the next twenty years, and the work came none too soon, for even by 1921 the possibility of transcontinental air travel was growing. In 1917 a Handley-Page bomber had flown from England to a Mediterranean base to bomb Constantinople. It had covered nearly 2000 miles in the process and had been airborne for a total of 31 hr. In 1919 Alcock and Brown in a Vickers-Vimy had made their historic first non-stop Atlantic crossing, and in the same year a de Havilland DH9 aircraft flying from Martlesham, in Suffolk, had been taken to a height of over 30 000 ft.

So by the early 1920s heavier-than-air machines had already covered distances and reached heights which would be commonplace for military and civil flying within fifteen years. Only speeds remained low and this deficiency was decisively rectified by the Schneider Trophy influence. To the engineers there was thus little doubt of the conditions under which automatic controls would eventually have to operate but opinions on how soon certain events would occur varied widely. Even Sir John Alcock expected the airship to be the only practical mode of transatlantic passenger flight for many years, a view perhaps not surprising when his own hazardous crossing is recalled.

By 1927 the work of Meredith, Cooke, and others was well advanced, and flight testing was being undertaken by aircraft other than purely experimental types. The earliest test of a gyro control on a transport aircraft is believed to have been when Vickers fitted such a unit to their Vanguard biplane prototype of 1923 vintage. A report on the first tests is still in existence and contains an important result which is described in these words:

> The first flight of the aircraft using the Gyro Rudder control was on the 29th April, 1927, when it was flown by Major J. S. J. Payn for 20 minutes. Twelve minutes after the commencement of the flight the necessary operation was carried out to put the gyro control in action but without success.
>
> Subsequent flights of 1 hour 5 minutes and 1 hour 50 minutes to Gosport via Winchester and return via Lympne were made for Air Ministry and Marconi tests. An attempt was again made to engage the gyro and this time, and on three other subsequent efforts the gyro control took complete and very definite charge. Satisfactory automatic control existed only in relatively calm air where slow correction was required. In such air conditions the machine could hold the gyro set course indefinitely as far as the control was concerned. In bumps of normal severity the automatic control was far from satisfactory insomuch as the lag in response was such that an increasing oscillation in yaw was set up terminating in a too vigorous action and a tendency to use up the full travel of the gyro control which roughly approximated to 5/8ths of the free foot control.

The report then went on to say that the directional stability of the Vanguard itself was poor and that this deficiency reduced the effectiveness of the gyro rudder. Subsequently a change of fin and rudder made a great improvement and this was significant for it gave an early demonstration of how automatic flying controls had to be matched to aeroplanes capable of responding to their demands; and vice versa, an illustration, in fact, of the main problem of control design whether for aircraft or for other uses.

192

Official recognition of the progress of automatic flight came in 1930 when the Air Staff specified automatic pilots for day bombers. There was still a need to build up confidence in the system for night operations or for entrusting dozens of civil airliner passengers to its care, but if a severe test was sought it came in the years 1931 to 1933, thanks to an attempt by the Royal Air Force on the world long distance record. The Fairey Aviation Company had in 1929 completed the construction of the Long Range

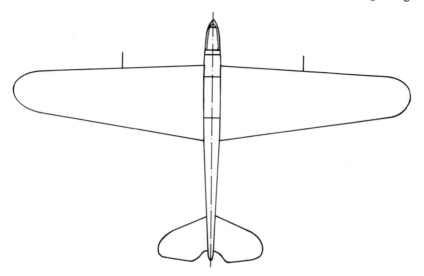

Figure 16. Plan view of Fairey long-range monoplane of 1933 which gained the world's distance record with a flight of 5300 miles. In doing so it gave a convincing demonstration of the use of automatic flying controls long before they became essential for supersonic flight.

monoplane (Fig. 16), but after some exploratory flights, it subsequently crashed in Africa, unfortunately killing the crew. It was decided, however, to construct a second aircraft of the type and to include in its equipment an automatic pilot. With this aircraft it was hoped to cover a distance greater than 5000 miles non-stop and calculations had shown that Walvis Bay in South Africa might be reached (not Cape Town as is sometimes erroneously stated): the pilot was to be Squadron Leader O. R. Gayford and the navigator Flight Lieutenant G. E. Nicholetts (following the death of another navigator originally selected). At first the automatic pilot was intended only for operating the elevators and rudder but Gayford soon found that the ailerons would also have to be included in the system, and in his own words:

> . . . the aircraft is found to be very cumbersome to fly, particularly in bumpy weather. This cumbersomeness is due to the general sluggishness of the controls. When a wing is dropped due to a bump a large yaw is set up, and this requires considerable application of top rudder and opposite aileron to counteract. A continual repetition of this over a long period would have the effect of appreciably reducing the aircraft's airspeed and will thus reduce its total range. Subsidiary results of this will be fatigue on pilots, and difficulty in steering a correct course.

In this statement is expressed all the need for automatic control at that time, and commenting in more detail, Gayford went on to say:

> . . . It is felt that the lateral instability of the aircraft, which causes it to drop a wing in bumps, with the resulting rudder and aileron movements necessary to counteract this . . . may prove too much for the automatic pilot to compete with. From the limited experience gained at present, it is believed that the degree of uncontrollability, set up by the bumps to be expected in Egypt and the Sudan, will prove more than the automatic pilot can cope with. It may, therefore, be necessary to consider the necessity of fitting a three-axis automatic control after further experience has been gained during the Egypt flight.

The reference here to Egypt describes some preliminary flying to be undertaken prior to the record attempt, which is now a piece of history. Taking off from Cranwell on 6 February 1933, Gayford and Nicholetts reached Walvis Bay, a distance of 5309 miles, in 57 hr 25 min, and landed on 8 February (NOTE: Britain then possessed the world's absolute flying records for both speed and distance). The automatic pilot proved most valuable and in his report of the flight Gayford wrote:

> The automatic control ran for 34 hours before finally going out of action. . . . Although it went out of action at an awkward time I do not think this need be taken as a serious reflection on its capabilities. I think the automatic control has a great future before it. . . . In this case it was doing a very difficult task. It was asked to run for 60 hours. Whereas its normal role is to run for six to eight hours and then on landing it received expert maintenance . . . the actual cause of failure, we discovered on return to England was quite a simple one. A deposit of congealed oil on a choke jet.

The possibility of such a failure might well have been uncovered by modern environmental testing, and as a final comment on just how hard the automatic pilot had had to work, he wrote of the conditions following its failure:

A considerable distance must have been lost during the night owing to constant yawing which it was found impossible to check. On many occasions the aircraft yawed over 90° off the desired course. . . . Had the weather been bumpy, I am convinced that we could not have kept the aircraft in control for the whole night.

Gayford unfortunately died in 1945 but his navigator, now Air Marshal Sir Gilbert Nicholetts, KBE, CB, AFC, RAF (Rtd), in a letter to the author recalled his long-range flight and subsequent experiences by saying of the automatic pilot:

My recollection is that when it was functioning it did so extremely well and I had as much confidence in it as I did in later years when I flew many hours on Sunderlands. I think the RAE did a good job on this device.

The Royal Air Force in the early 1930s thus became a pioneer large-scale user of automatic pilots, to be followed slightly later by the civil airlines who, being naturally more cautious, benefited from the military experience. Specialized functions requiring extreme steadiness of flight were also, with advantage, given over to automatic control, aerial survey being an example from which much clearer photographs were obtained in far less time and with far less pilot effort than hitherto. Eventually aircraft were able to use their auto pilots not only for level flight but also to perform simple manoeuvres such as turns, and during World War II vast numbers of them, so equipped, brought automatic flight to its first peak of development. Then, following great advances in electronics and servo-mechanisms, a new range of electrically operated auto pilots came to be constructed. They were lighter in weight, more sensitive, and less bulky than their mechanical predecessors, and if speed increases had been the only outcome of the jet-propulsion revolution then automatic flight might, for many years, have entailed merely the use of these new units in the existing navigational and manoeuvring roles.

But jet flight nearly doubled the average aircraft operating height; it also established high Mach number effects as being inevitable byproducts of high performance, and it was these two changes of aerodynamic environment more than any other which complicated the progress of automatic flight. In both cases the problem was one of stability. At high altitudes the air density could be as little as one-fifth that at sea-level, and just as a ball will bounce up and down in water but not in a more dense liquid like

195

mercury, so, in the thin upper atmosphere, any disturbance of an aircraft tended to damp out slowly if indeed it damped at all. In extreme cases, and the deH.108 was an example of this as we saw in Chapter 4, a violent oscillation could occur at any altitude and could even build up rather than damp out.

For the most part, however, pitching, rolling, and yawing motions were experienced similar to those felt when rowing a small boat across ripples on a lake, and even these, unless eliminated, could be detrimental to such military actions as weapon aiming or to the economics and comfort of passenger aircraft. The damping devices, known as autostabilizers, were therefore developed which moved either the main flying controls, or special tabs, continuously through small angles in opposition to any motion. To get some idea of what this entailed imagine trying to use the oars of a rowing-boat for hours on end to prevent it rocking from side to side!

As far as Mach number effects were concerned the large changes of trim which could accompany even a small change of Mach number were certain to be a serious burden if continuously occurring on long flights, so automatic trimmers were introduced which sensed Mach number through its component parts of speed and altitude. In contrast to the autostabilizer these mechanisms sometimes had to make quite large control movements but were just as continuously needed for their function of maintaining trim.

So a full cycle of events was completed for it was to ensure stability that automatic controls had first been proposed, rather than to ease the job of the pilot, and this function was now to be added to their existing duties. It was, however, in circumstances quite undreamed of by the pioneers, and in recognition of the comprehensive nature of modern automatic flight, its various elements came to be described collectively by the term 'flight control system', the name auto pilot being no longer adequate. The V-bombers conformed to the new pattern; it fact it might be said that they more than conformed for their flying controls were in any case fully powered and the automatic element was thus routed through the power control motors and not directly to the control surfaces. Even the first big American jets such as the B52 and Boeing 707 possessed basically manual controls, so, whereas in the early days of jet-powered fighters, Britain had been slow in departing from conventional control systems, the thinking was very much reversed on the larger and more expensive bombers.

Such radically new ideas and equipment of course called for more elaborate test programmes. The main problem was assessing the consequences of control failure, and considering that numerous untried devices were all at one time or another trying to operate the same set of control surfaces it was to be expected that conflicts would arise. If two people are pushing one another and one unexpectedly moves out of the way the other is liable to fall with a bang. The aim therefore was to try to get all parts of a flight control system to move as expected. What would happen if one part suddenly failed or was mistakenly switched off? The only way to find out was to feed in deliberate failures during airborne tests and this sometimes hair-raising technique was extensively developed. The Aeroplane and Armament Experimental Establishment at Boscombe Down played a leading role in establishing safety standards, particularly in the mid-1950s, when the V-bombers were undergoing their service release trials. In certain cases restrictions had to be placed on the use of automatic devices in order to provide adequate safety margins and it was often very difficult to assess the chances of containing a failure. Imagine a test pilot embarking on a sortie to investigate automatic control failures. He knows the purpose of the tests, and if a crew member tries to catch him unawares by feeding in a failure without warning he is in current practice to deal with the situation. Corrective action was taken only after about a two seconds' delay to try and simulate the element of surprise, but, even so, could the exercise quite be equated to an average pilot, perhaps tired after a long flight and happily relaxed under automatic control in his previously trustworthy aircraft, suddenly being confronted with a violent motion the like of which might only be experienced once in a lifetime? The responsibility for briefing flight test crews for these experiments was considerable. The worst dangers could not always be predicted from simulated failures, as real failures sometimes occurred which ground rig tests had shown to be 'impossible'. The fitting of extensive test instrumentation of course went a long way to explaining the behaviour of control systems, but it could not prevent immediate failures even though it might show how to avoid future disasters. Test pilots' observations, far from being supplanted by the vast quantities of data provided by modern recording apparatus, were essential in deciding how much authority an automatic device should be allowed to have in the interests of safety.

Safety depended very much on the time available to appreciate if a dangerous situation was arising, and prolonged arguments ranged over the

197

provision of warnings to show the pilot which part of a complex control system had failed or was about to fail. Flashing lights, bells, hooters, and small flags all found a place in various aircraft, but they themselves could fail and some pilots strongly resisted cluttering up an already overloaded cockpit with devices of arguable value. As with powered controls, the answer was of course to aim for extreme reliability and this has now been achieved.

The extent to which the V-bombers put Britain on the road to even more advanced projects can perhaps best be appreciated by mentioning that on numerous occasions Royal Air Force crews have flown these aircraft into high placings in the American Strategic Air Command bombing competitions. Taking on the cream of the United States Air Force on their own familiar territory, they have proved equal to the best. Nearer home Vulcan XA 899, on 22 December 1959, at the RAE Bedford, became the first four-jet aircraft in the world to be landed fully automatically and the Vulcan is still in front line service.

But if the V-bombers marked the start of the automatic flight control era, they also marked the end of what might be called its mechanical beginning. Automatic flight was, in the first instance, mostly a matter of mechanical engineering with controls connected by mechanical linkages and operated by hydraulic and pneumatic actuating systems. These were relatively heavy and were liable to distortion due both to changes of temperature and to bending of the aircraft structure. They were therefore of limited accuracy. The final mechanism for moving a control surface or other device would of course always have to be mechanical, at least in part, but what could be changed was the means of transmitting the pilot's or other demands to the control. If this could be done electrically the drawbacks of mechanical systems could mostly be overcome. The problem here, however, was, once again, reliability, and a start had to be made by constructing and testing what became popularly known as a 'fly-by-wire' system.

The first-known airborne fly-by-wire experiments were, in fact, British, and were undertaken under Government contract by Boulton Paul Aircraft Limited, whose name we have already mentioned in connection with their excellent work on early powered flying controls and delta winged aircraft.

The aircraft used was a Vickers Viscount airliner fitted with two Rolls-Royce Tay jet engines (Photograph 46) in place of the normal four

Photograph 46. Vickers Viscount fitted with Rolls-Royce Tay engines. This aircraft was used by Boulton Paul Limited for the first known tests of a 'fly-by-wire' flight control system.
(British Aerospace)

Rolls-Royce Dart turboprops. This conversion was originally used as an engine test bed and then in support of the Valiant bomber programme. The fly-by-wire experiments began in 1957, one set of pilot's controls being operated in the normal way, and the other by the experimental system. This of course was for safety reasons. Over two years the Tay Viscount made twenty flights, totalling 21 hr flying, of which half was under fly-by-wire control, and pilots who flew it were unanimous in their praise.

Enough had then been learned to apply the principle to an aircraft of much higher performance, and the Viscount experiments were quickly followed by tests at the RAE, using one of the small Avro 707 delta aircraft, the two-seat 707C, in order that fly-by-wire and normal control systems could again be available for safety reasons, as in the Viscount.

199

Photograph 47. VC.10. This particular aircraft, built for East African Airways, was the last of the type produced and is shown here after completion at Weybridge. It was also the last complete aircraft made at this historic site, scene of aviation pioneering and of motor racing on the Brooklands Track.
(British Aerospace)

Some time later a two-seat Hawker Hunter was brought into the fly-by-wire programme, with similarly excellent results. Today, fly-by-wire is in operational use particularly in the United States where it has been applied to both aircraft and Space vehicles.

As if to ring down the curtain on the first twenty years of jet-propelled flight, Britain produced an aircraft which represented all that had been learned of multi-jet design in that period. Known as the VC.10 (Photograph 47) by its creators, Vickers-Armstrongs (Aircraft) Limited, it was intended as a long-range airliner for Commonwealth routes, but was soon given a transatlantic capability, and at the time of its construction was the largest aircraft programme to be undertaken alone by any country in Europe. The VC.10 incorporated fully powered controls and full automatic flight facilities, thereby becoming the most advanced aircraft of its class in the world, but, unfortunately, its career was limited by political

Cambridge he worked under the direction of the renowned Professor Melville Jones and gained further insight of experimental techniques which later proved useful. Whittle's name is mentioned in a report on drag measurements carried out by the Cambridge University Aeronautics Laboratory in 1935 – a paragraph from the preface written by Melville Jones reads:

> Wind tunnel experiments preliminary to those described in Section III were carried out by myself in the early months of 1935, but the whole of the experiments recorded in that section were made by Flight Lieutenant F. Whittle, working entirely alone. This Officer is attending the R.A.F. Officers Course at Cambridge University.

One day in 1935, when the hazy, lazy days of a pre-war British summer with its tennis parties, tea dances, picnics and, for some, flying meetings were about to begin, two ex-Royal Air Force Officers, J. C. B. Tinling and R. D. Williams, approached Whittle with a proposal for trying to convert his jet engine plans into a workable form. Williams had earlier served with Whittle, both at Cranwell and later at Felixstowe, so was fully conversant with his ideas. Together Tinling and Williams became Whittle's business advisers and set about putting things on a practical basis.

(By coincidence it was in 1935 that the jet engine's future aerodynamic ally, the swept wing, was first emphasized as a means of achieving supersonic flight. This was during Professor Büsemann's previously mentioned address to the Volta Conference.)

Whittle's own hopes were not high but he saw an opportunity, however slight, of making some progress, and a firm of investment bankers, O. T. Falk and Partners, was approached for finance. This resulted in the formation during March 1936 of Power Jets Limited, with the object of designing, manufacturing, and testing an experimental jet engine to Whittle's plans. The assistance of the British Thomson-Houston Company Limited of Rugby was sought, and an order placed with them in June 1936 for making most of the parts. An exception was the combustion chamber, the requirements for which were extreme enough to deter most possible manufacturers from participating in what, had they known it, was to become one of this century's greatest engineering adventures. Eventually Laidlaw, Drew and Company of Edinburgh undertook the combustion chamber design, so completing the chain of actions needed to launch the new technology.

During all this Whittle sat his Tripos examinations at Cambridge, and gained a First, after which the Air Ministry allowed him to stay on for a further year so that work on the engine could continue.

By 12 April 1937 the first engine had been completed and was ready for test. Initial running showed deficiencies in both compressor performance and combustion, but nobody expected miracles and a certain satisfaction was expressed with the results. Up to the outbreak of war, in 1939, three experimental engines had been built and considerable insight gained into the nature of various problems. Even so, in a report written in 1937, Dr Griffith said of Power Jets work:

> It is of value only for special purposes such as the attainment of high speed or high altitude for a short time in cases where take-off requirements are not stringent.

This seemingly unenthusiastic statement by its undoubtedly able author might have been more generous had war been a little nearer. In such circumstances high speed and high altitude were to be of paramount importance and economy of little concern. It seems likely that had Griffith's own work not been restricted between 1930 and 1937, the RAE might also have been forced into developing a pure jet engine to satisfy military needs instead of investigating the economy seeking, propeller driving, variant.

Whatever one might think in retrospect, it happened that by 1939 the Air Ministry had seen in Whittle's project the possibility of creating practical jet aircraft. A contract was thus placed with Power Jets on 12 July of that year to build an engine intended not, as before, for ground testing but actually for flight. This event marked both a turning point in the original research and the beginning of an era whose influence would be comparable to, and possibly greater than, that of the earlier Industrial Revolution. In fact, the world is still in the throes of a technological upheaval, the duration of which is hard to predict. One thing is certain, the speed-up of airborne communication, made possible by jet engines, has given considerable impetus to other technologies, notably electronics. If, therefore, one should, in future years, ask when and where the Technological Revolution began, one might say on 12 July 1939, in Britain – the day when Power Jets Limited were contracted to build their first jet-propulsion engine for flight.

Power Jets called this new engine, of 850 lb thrust, the W1, and the Gloster Aircraft Company were asked to construct an aircraft to accom-

Photograph 49. The Gloster E28/39 fitted with the first Whittle jet-propulsion engine. This was the first British jet-propelled aircraft.
(Royal Aircraft Establishment – Crown Copyright)

modate it. This was designed to Specification E28/39. There was by then no question that a major war was likely to start and, as with most other early airborne experiments concerned with transonic flight, the conflict supplied at least one good reason why progress should be rapid.

Taxi-ing trials of the E28/39, which is shown in Photograph 49, commenced in April 1941. During the course of these a short hop was made. The need for secrecy had prompted the authorities to select RAF Cranwell as the base for trials, the place where, thirteen years earlier, Whittle as a Cadet had written his original thesis including a study of jet propulsion. He thus saw, on the same spot, his ideas take wing. The first flight proper occurred on 14 May 1941, with the late P. E. G. Sayer as pilot. During the following fourteen days initial testing was completed satisfactorily.

It need hardly be said that the possibility of using jet-propelled aircraft in combat received urgent consideration. The stages in the process cannot be better expressed than by quoting Whittle's own words:

> . . . at the beginning of 1940 the Air Ministry (later the Ministry of Aircraft Production) began to work on the assumption that there was a good chance of getting jet propelled fighter aircraft into production in time for use in the war. As a result the following steps were taken:
> 1. Power Jets were authorised to go ahead with a more advanced engine (the 'W2').
> 2. The Gloster Aircraft Company was authorised to proceed with the design of a twin engined interceptor fighter (the F9/40 – prototype of the Meteor).
> 3. Direct contracts were placed with the British Thomson-Houston Company and other firms for the manufacture and development of jet propulsion gas turbines.
> 4. It was decided that Power Jets should become a research and development organisation and that they were to supply all other firms engaged with all necessary drawings and any other information they needed to assist them in their work.

Before the end of 1941 it could therefore truly be said that a new industry had arisen in Britain when plans were made for the production of both Whittle's engines and Meteor fighters. An organization known as the Gas Turbine Collaboration Committee was also set up to co-ordinate the activities and thinking of those concerned in the new venture. Its Chairman, Dr H. Roxbee Cox (now Lord Kings-Norton), has said that his direction of this Committee was the activity of which he was most proud, and such a statement from one of the industry's most eminent engineers is surely a measure of the contribution made by the British in this field. But that was not all. In the autumn of 1941 a team of Power Jets engineers, complete with an engine and design drawings, went to America and gave to that country the essentials of jet engine construction. They had really started something!

On the face of it the Whittle story had all the ingredients of a classic novel illustrating the rewards of hard work and dedication. The degree of success was probably greater than even a most imaginative author might dream up and the consequent possession by Britain of a massive new industry necessitated national, as well as commercial, planning. The results were not pleasing to Power Jets Limited. In 1941 a research and development station for gas turbines was constructed for the RAE at Pyestock and, under the direction of the late Hayne Constant, commenced work in 1942. This unit was a separate Turbine Division of the main

Engine Experimental Department, and eventually, in 1944, was combined with Power Jets Limited, to form Power Jets (Research and Development) Limited, the whole being government controlled. It would be pointless to comment here on any rights or wrongs of this virtual nationalization of Whittle's strong and intensely individualistic team. The full details are available from many other sources. Suffice it to say that many of the original personnel later broke away and kept the company name going, both as consultants and in the running of an excellent School of Gas Turbine Technology, in the old Farnborough Manor House, which is now St Peter's School, but eventually the firm was wound up – almost exactly forty years after the writing of Whittle's original thesis. A last relic of this historic organization, a small test house, can still be seen near the entrance to the present National Gas Turbine Establishment at Pyestock. Ironically it is just across the road from the massive new RAE structural test building for Concorde, which symbolizes all that has been made possible by over forty years of British jet engine development.

In April 1937, when Power Jets' first experimental engine started running, the RAE Farnborough sought approval to resume its own work on gas turbine engines. A Technical Note on this subject, entitled 'The Internal Combustion Turbine as a Power Plant for Aircraft', was written by Hayne Constant and discussed at length the prospects in this field. Some of Griffith's earlier suggestions were restated and, for the benefit of the doubters, the following forceful words written:

> The very magnitude of the advantages which it has to offer, associated with the repeated failures to achieve a practicable design, have given the impression that the Internal Combustion Turbine is merely a convenient medium on which to work off the surplus energy of imaginative inventors. In fact, however, the same principles and same practical experiences as have in the past predicted the performance of machines of far more novel design, can be applied to determine the probable success or failure of the internal combustion turbine.

This was after all a time when aviation, despite the lessons of World War I, still appeared to many as a plaything; when science fiction penetrated receptive minds with predictions of 'death rays' and devices of similar powers. Only those closely associated with particular scientific disciplines had any idea of their potential, pent up by years of economic depression and the fear of unwittingly contributing to a future war. In the end it was the advent of war clouds which stimulated gas turbine activity. In the 87th report of the Engine Sub-Committee of the Aeronautical

Research Committee, in May 1937, the work of both Whittle and the RAE was the subject of these recommendations:

The Engine Sub-Committee recommend the Air Ministry should take up the question of the development of the internal combustion turbine as a matter of urgency and make all possible arrangements for its production at the earliest possible moment. They consider that this will probably require the co-operation of turbine builders and recommend that the possibilities in this direction should be explored without delay.

The firm of Metropolitan-Vickers Limited was favoured as a collaborator in this scheme, with the result that after a visit by RAE personnel on 3 June 1937, the mechanism of joint working was established. Over the next two years numerous compressor and turbine systems were tested, and in September 1939 the RAE suggested to Power Jets Limited the use of an axial compressor in a pure jet engine. A design known as the F1 was produced and sent to Power Jets but they soon decided that their other work did not allow time to pursue an axial compressor project. Metropolitan-Vickers therefore took it over in a modified form known as the F2. This became the first practical axial flow engine to fly and is shown in Photograph 50a. It still looks remarkably modern although completed in November 1941 and first run the following month (compare with modern Spey engine, Photograph 50b.) All it lacked was an aircraft in which to fly. Ideally, a Meteor would have been the test vehicle but none was available, so the F2 was first airborne in 1943 in the tail of a Lancaster test bed and gave cause for considerable satisfaction (Photograph 51).

One other early British gas turbine family should be mentioned which although not forming part of the original research effort nevertheless played a major part in launching both the Royal Air Force and civil airlines into the jet age. In 1941 the de Havilland Company's aero-engine organization, led by the late Frank Halford, embarked upon the design of jet engines, following the success of Whittle's work. By April 1942 the first of these was ready for test bed running. Known initially as the H1, but subsequently as the Goblin, it was a centrifugal compressor type. Being the product of an existing large engineering unit the Goblin possessed a big advantage when it came to translating a prototype into mass production form. It thus happened that Halford's Goblin became the first British production jet engine to fly and the H1 prototypes powered the first Gloster Meteor for its early flying after other engines had suffered delays. Apart from supplying power for de Havilland's own Vampire

Photograph 50a. Metropolitan Vickers F2 of 1941. The first British jet engine to be flown with an axial flow compressor. Its modern appearance can be appreciated by comparison with a much later engine shown in Photograph 50b.
(Royal Aircraft Establishment – Crown Copyright)

217

Photograph 50b. Rolls-Royce Spey engine currently in world-wide service. (Rolls-Royce)

218

Photograph 51. Metropolitan Vickers F2 jet engine mounted in tail of the first prototype Lancaster Bomber BT 308.
(Royal Aircraft Establishment – Crown Copyright)

fighter and the legendary Type 108, a similar but more powerful development, the Ghost, was installed in the Comet airliner, so becoming the first pure jet engine in the world to enter scheduled passenger airline service.

Once jet engines had passed from the experimental to the practical stage some applications of their capabilities attracted the most intense study. The demands of war then dictated that speed rather than economy should be of immediate interest. Post-war plans for military jet engines naturally followed this trend while civil requirements sought out the original aim of improved fuel consumption. On the experimental side, a highly ambitious scheme was put in hand to provide power for supersonic research, particularly for the Miles M52 aircraft. In the exciting transition period of the late 1940s the foundations of a tremendously successful gas turbine industry were in fact laid – let us therefore continue this chapter by describing the follow-up to the pioneer work at a time when the conquest of supersonic flight dominated the aviation scene.

By 1942 British jet engine technology was well established and, although the stark simplicity of early engines was much emphasized, some increase of complexity was to be expected in future, more advanced types. Many possible developments were visualized and active design work commenced. Tribute to the overall effort was expressed in many quarters but a cautious word was sounded by Sir Roy Fedden, who, in delivering the Thirty-Second Wilbur Wright Memorial Lecture to the Royal Aeronautical Society on 25 May 1944, said:

> There is no doubt that this country has established a permanent place for herself in the history of the development of this new prime mover, and we owe a debt of gratitude to Group Captain Whittle and his colleagues, and also the RAE and the firms who have co-operated, for the vision and effort which has been demanded to overcome the difficulties and disappointments which have preceded the practical application of the continuous combustion turbine power plant.
>
> We in Great Britain must not forget, however, that extensive developments on gas turbines and jet propulsion are taking place on the Continent and in America and it is important that we should not rest on our laurels but show the same resourcefulness and initiative in bringing our successful prototypes to regular series production as we have evinced during the initial stages of development.

Happily, for once, Britain did not allow others to cash in on its hard work, so the aero-engine industry became, and has so far remained, a mainstay of British engineering export markets, but only thanks to a bold decision of a type which in recent years has sadly become more difficult.

After the début of the first jet engines the next major step was to bring axial flow compressor designs into commission. This was a much disputed policy, thought by some to be premature. Was there not a vast experience of centrifugal compressors? Would it not be better to consolidate existing gains before a change of strategy? We can once again quote the late Hayne Constant to describe this situation. Delivering the second Sir Henry Royce Memorial Lecture to the Royal Aeronautical Society on 4 November 1957, he spoke of work at Pyestock, both before and after the formation of the National Gas Turbine Establishment, and said:

> Right from the very beginning of our work there was one basic concept in our philosophy that conditioned our general thinking. This concept was the vital importance in engineering development of making a sufficiently concentrated effort on a small front to keep ahead of all competitors. . . . This is not an easy policy to adopt; hedging requires far less thought. It is a dangerous policy, because if you back the wrong horse you have nothing else to turn to; but if your judgement is good it gives great advantages.
>
> The first example of this attitude was our decision . . . to abandon the centrifugal compressor of which we had quite a lot of experience, and to concentrate entirely on the unproven axial type.

A new generation of centrifugal compressor engines was nevertheless born to power some of the early post-war military and experimental aeroplanes described in Chapter 3. Rolls-Royce having produced the Welland (Photograph 52) from Whittle's basic layout, then offered more power with the Derwent and Nene – many of which are still in service. From de Havilland came uprated Goblins and the previously mentioned Ghost. Numerous speed and height records owe their existence to these engines which also found a ready market abroad.

But despite the initial runaway growth of jet propulsion, rocket power seemed at first to be the only sure way to supersonic flight in the immediate future, and it would have been easy to leave the narrow path of progressive jet engine development in pursuit of this aim. In terms of post war markets it was fortunate for the British that this did not happen.

From the very early days both Whittle and the RAE gas turbine research team had, as we have said, understood the principles of some possible variations on the simple jet engine theme. Depending on the requirements, these were aimed at increased thrust, improved fuel consumption, or both. The translation of ideas into reality depended, as ever, on the available materials, but wartime influences greatly accelerated

Photograph 52. Rolls-Royce Welland jet engine. A typical early unit similar to Sir Frank Whittle's first prototype engines.
(Rolls-Royce)

the search for extra thrust. To this end reheat seemed attractive, the advantage of burning fuel in the jet pipe in this way being that it gave significantly increased thrust without greatly raising the severely limited turbine temperature and could be selected only when needed, say, for take-off or combat manoeuvres. Disadvantages were that fuel consumption increased considerably, particularly at subsonic speeds, but, more important, the extra thrust could only be gained by temporarily increasing the jet pipe outlet area while reheat was operating. This involved the complication and weight of a suitable operating mechanism, but this alone did not ensure satisfactory operation, for serious combustion problems arose when trying to light and maintain the reheat flame as height increased. Despite this limitation, however, a special circumstance called for its early use at the low altitudes where it did work.

In 1943 the first reheat experiments were conducted on the ground at Pyestock, and the Ministry of Aircraft Production, encouraged by the results, decided to follow these with airborne tests. These commenced at the RAE Farnborough in 1944 and the results were of far more than academic interest. Defence against the flying bomb depended on aircraft of the highest possible speed and even the first Meteor jet fighters were barely able to keep pace with the German pilotless missiles, so reheat was of immediate operational significance.

A Meteor Mark I, fitted with Power Jets' W2/B23 engines, was thus modified with a reheat fuel and ignition system, and, after some preliminary flying, embarked upon the main test programme. Due to the urgent nature of the experiments, a crew of two was carried by fitting a temporary seat behind the pilot in a space normally occupied by ammunition tanks. By this means a scientist occupying the seat was able to concentrate on assessing the behaviour of reheat during flight, thus economizing in flying and analysis time.

A programme of thirty flights was undertaken for these first reheat tests. Only two flights failed to produce data, one when a broken wire prevented light-up and another when bad weather intervened. This was a remarkable success rate considering the limited knowledge and haste involved. Effective operation was obtained up to a height of 13 000 ft which, while low by later requirements, was more than enough for flying bomb interception. Reheat was used during the tests on average twice per flying hour, the following figures applying to tests on the starboard engine:

Flying time   18 hr 5 min
Reheat time   3 hr 33 min
Number of times reheat used   52

The approximate changes of performance were:

Thrust increase   25 per cent
Speed increase   45 miles/h
Rate of climb increase   40 per cent at sea-level
Fuel consumption increase 65 per cent.

Encouraging as these results were, however, there remained the problem of suddenly providing an increased jet pipe exit area during reheat light-up. Professor A. D. Baxter, at one time Professor of Aircraft Propulsion at the College of Aeronautics, Cranfield (and now retired as a Research Consultant), was then in charge of RAE reheat development and stated to the author:

At that time we had not developed a variable area nozzle. Effort was concentrated on a two position nozzle (normal and re-heat) but this did not have adequate mechanical reliability. It was suggested that the aircraft could fly with large fixed nozzles suitable for re-heat and accept the loss in performance at other times. Alternatively, a design was prepared for a normal nozzle which could be jettisoned when switching on re-heat. The larger nozzle this left in operation would then be used for the remainder of the flight.

By such extreme measures a temporary operational requirement might have been met but when the occupation of the flying bomb sites removed the threat from this source, the urgency behind reheat development disappeared and by this time the RAE experiments had been prematurely terminated, so that Power Jets Limited could improve the system for service use. It was, however, some years before reheat became a reliable and flexible tool. Now widely used in military aircraft it has also entered the civil scene with the advent of supersonic airliners.

Of the numerous other variations on the simple jet engine theme foreseen in the formative years, the bypass flow system and the multi-spool layout have been foremost in widening the scope of gas turbine operation. Whereas reheat meant having two combustion systems, bypass flow, as the name suggests, meant having two separate streams of air, one of which bypassed the main engine, and multi-spool designs contained two or more independently rotating compressor and turbine shafts. Combinations of all three have additionally been used.

Whittle saw the advantages of bypass flow as early as 1936 and in a patent specification described the process thus:

The primary object is to provide as great a mass-flow of the working fluid as possible . . . The high mass flow is particularly desirable in the case of the propulsion of aircraft by fluid reaction in order that the jet velocity shall be as low as possible.

In other words, by moving a larger quantity of gas slowly instead of a small quantity quickly, greater propulsive efficiency would be obtained. The RAE workers did not initially have Whittle's need for such schemes. They intended to use a normal propeller anyway and it was only when embarking on pure jet work that bypass flows were relevant. Their efforts were then mostly devoted to ducted fan derivatives. In this design the extra quantity of propulsive air, outside the normal hot jet gases, was captured not by a large diameter compressor stage but by a fan revolving in a duct around the main engine by which it was driven. This arrangement was a half-way stage between the pure jet and turbo-propeller engines.

Both pure bypass and ducted fan layouts were, and are, primarily useful at subsonic speeds, giving improved take-off thrust and fuel consumption together with noise reduction advantages. Their bulk and weight, however, tend to limit their use for supersonic flight.

Although bypass engines were not running until the 1950s, work on ducted fans commenced about 1942, and after preliminary trials at the RAE on a small test rig, Metropolitan-Vickers built and tested a ducted fan engine, the F3, the following year. Power Jets Limited were then also busy with numerous schemes of this nature but none so interesting as their proposal for an engine to power the Miles M52 supersonic research aircraft. For this project no engine available or under immediate development possessed anything like enough thrust, so a proposal was made to take the latest Whittle engine, the W2/700, and add to it a modification known as the Number 4 thrust augmenter. This was a ducted fan with additional fuel burning downstream of the fan, giving effectively two engines in one.

Three previous augmenter designs had been subjected to limited testing, some of it disappointing. The frenzied outpouring of ideas which characterized this period was, however, so coloured by earlier success that great expectations surrounded almost any new proposal. In a remarkably forward-looking report in February 1944, the suggested Miles M52 power plant was described by Power Jets Limited in the following words.

The power plant consists of a Power Jets Limited W2/700 unit as prime mover. The exhaust energy from the unit is used partly to drive the augmenter and partly to provide thrust. The augmenter is of the two-stage type, the two stages rotating together. After passing through the augmenter fan which is outside the turbine, the by-pass air is heated in combustion chambers before being discharged through the propelling nozzle. The two gas streams from the engine and from the augmenter fan are kept separate and pass through two concentric propelling nozzles both of which are of fixed area. Control is effected by means of the usual engine throttle, together with a shut off valve for the by-pass fuel. The latter fuel is controlled automatically.

225

How well this particular system would have worked will never be known for it never flew. The author has heard several opinions on its likely success expressed by some of those concerned; one of the problems being how to keep the gas flows separate, but the intended performance is still of interest and is now described.

At 36 000 ft and within the temperature limits set by the materials of construction, aircraft speeds up to 1000 miles/h were considered. At the highest speed a calculated thrust of 4000 lb had to be available which would have given a fuel consumption of 8000 lb/h. If the drag of an M52 or similar aircraft had been low enough to realize the required speed, would the fuel capacity have allowed a worthwhile flight time? Later experiences with the supersonic Bristol 188 Gyron Junior Combination proved initially disappointing in this respect and showed the difficulties of estimating supersonic performance. It is thus conceivable that Power Jets' much earlier effort might have fallen short of expectations but what cannot be denied is the spirit, optimism, and self-confidence which enabled such a design to be undertaken at a time when the simplest jet propulsion techniques had barely been mastered elsewhere.

Multi-spool engines formed an even earlier line of research than bypass systems, but not until 1943 was serious design commenced at the RAE. This work still centred mainly on the turbo-propeller combination rather than pure jet propulsion but certain mechanical problems were common to both. The aim was to obtain high compression ratios without experiencing starting and blade stalling problems, which some thought would arise with single-spool axial compressors of high performance. Although difficulties of this nature did arise and were overcome by such means as tapping off air and employing variable angle compressor blades, it was originally believed that axial flow designs would operate only within narrow limits. By splitting the compressor into two or more parts, each driven by a separate turbine, the speed of each part could be matched to the degree of compression demanded at various power outputs. In a sense this was like avoiding indigestion by eating in small mouthfuls rather than in one large gulp. Pilots could then operate the throttles rapidly without risking engine stoppage, an ability lacking in early jet engines and of particular importance during landing. In fact early foreign jet engines failed to match the operating flexibility of British designs, and after the important decision to pursue the multi-spool system had been taken, the production of a satisfactory prototype added yet another achievement to a long list.

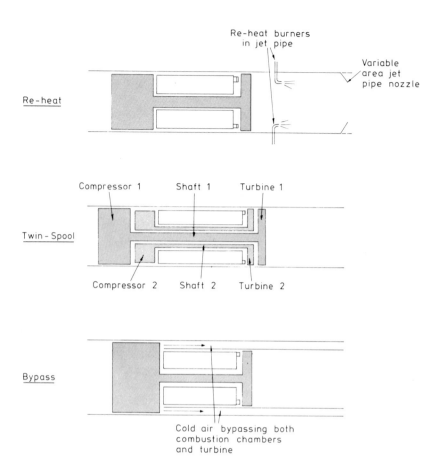

Figure 18. Types of jet-propulsion engine.

Figure 18 shows, in diagrammatic form, a layout of each type of jet engine so far mentioned. We have dealt with their early history at some length because they represented a singularly British contribution to high-speed flight. We conclude this chapter by describing briefly some modern jet engine families which have gained both national and international fame.

227

It is not often appreciated that the traditional British aircraft engine builders had little to do with early gas turbine development. This situation arose both from an urgent need to supply large quantities of military piston engines and from a lack of turbine design experience. Firms such as Metropolitan-Vickers with their tradition of turbine manufacture assisted greatly in the embryo stage, but in 1944 it was foreseen that they and others might not wish to continue in aircraft work, so some reappraisal of the future was made within the Ministry of Aircraft Production. The post-war aero-engine industry would obviously not support too many rivals in the field. Plans for the construction of massive piston engines were therefore abandoned in favour of jet development by organizations such as Rolls-Royce, Bristol, de Havilland, and Armstrong-Siddeley, backed up by the facilities of RAE, NGTE, and various university research units.

Following their early participation in producing Whittle engines, Rolls-Royce, who had in 1939 acquired the services of Dr Griffith, took up the challenge of axial flow compressors and produced two major designs, the Avon and the Conway. The former, with reheat, having powered both the Fairey Delta 2 and the production Lightning fighters, can claim a lion's share of the credit for British supersonic progress both in aircraft and engine performance. Although possessing only a single-spool compressor, which benefited from Metropolitan-Vickers' work, the Avon has nevertheless been widely used for both military and civil purposes. The Conway, combining bypass with a twin-spool compressor design, has primarily served the civil market but a military version has effectively powered the Victor B Mk. 2 bomber. More recently, Rolls-Royce have produced the triple-spool RB.211 ducted fan engine family, and although these engines have attracted substantial orders, they were unfortunately involved in the financial collapse of the original Rolls-Royce organization.

The contribution from the one-time Bristol Engine organization has been, and still is, dominated by their outstanding Olympus twin-spool design. They came late into pure jet work and they had to devote much effort first to piston engines and later to engines for the monster but abortive Brabazon airliner and Princess flying-boat projects. When their team eventually considered a pure jet design, it decided not to copy existing trends but rather to develop a new type and make it their own. Having been much concerned with engines for larger aircraft, Bristols continued on this line and reviewed the needs of future bombers. Fuel economy was here important in the interests of long range. They selected a twin-spool layout to give the best overall characteristics and this became the Olympus. It first flew in a Canberra flying test bed on 5 August 1952, twice took the world altitude record, and was then selected to power the Vulcan bomber. This aircraft–engine combination proved a most fortuitous happening, both for the Bristol engineers and for Britain. The development of the Vulcan continually called for more engine power, and the Olympus, having started at a static thrust of 9000 lb, went to no less than 21 000 lb in this subsonic role. Then came the Supersonic Transport requirement, and for the Anglo–French Concorde a highly developed version of the Olympus engine was selected. Men unborn when it was designed will thus be supervising its maintenance and modification for many years to come, and this is a measure of the development potential obtained by good basic design.

Following the Olympus, Bristols produced the lightweight Orpheus, which powered not only the Gnat fighter and trainer but also a variety of types in other countries. Finally, before becoming part of the Rolls-Royce organization, Bristols brought to maturity the Pegasus ducted fan vectored-thrust engine for vertical take-off and landing (VTOL) operation. This most significant development first ran in 1959 and first flew in the Hawker-Siddeley P.1127 in October 1960. This aircraft evolved into the Harrier, the world's first operational VTOL combat machine. It possesses excellent handling qualities whether hovering just above the ground or diving supersonically, a creditable achievement for such a radically new concept.

Armstrong-Siddeley's major work was the Sapphire, a single-spool axial-flow engine. Developed in parallel with the Rolls-Royce Avon, on the old insurance policy basis, the Sapphire came by way of Metropolitan-Vickers who were originally asked to develop an engine similar to the Avon. This was called the F9, but in the post-war reorganization, Armstrong-Siddeley took over the project, performed some mechanical redesign, and so the Sapphire was born. Although overshadowed by its partner, the Avon, the Sapphire nevertheless powered the English Electric P1A when it became Britain's first level flight supersonic aircraft. It was installed in Royal Air Force Hunters, Javelins, and Victors of various marks as well as in Comets and the prototype Vulcan prior to the arrival of the Olympus. The Americans also took the Sapphire design, made it into their J65 and thus continued a tradition started by early Whittle engines.

229

The latter-day de Havilland contribution to high-speed power plants followed the philosophy of the times and Frank Halford aimed to produce:

(1) A large, high thrust, pure jet engine.

(2) A combined jet engine-rocket unit.

To satisfy the first aim he designed the Gyron, with an initial thrust of 15 000 lb and a capacity to attain 20 000 lb when further developed. There was no official specification for the Gyron so the Company initiated this project as a private venture. It first ran in January 1953 after which the Ministry of Supply eventually awarded de Havilland a development contract. A Short Sperrin bomber was used as a flying test bed in which a Gyron first flew in September 1955. Unfortunately no aircraft ever made use of the Gyron although with reheat a ground test thrust of 29 000 lb was attained.

The second of Halford's ideas was intended for use in a Saunders-Roe mixed power plant supersonic aircraft of which the SR.53, mentioned in Chapter 6, was a small-scale experimental version. For the full-sized machine a scaled-down Gyron, known as the Gyron Junior, was to have supplied the pure jet portion of the total power. This project was also doomed to overall cancellation but out of the debris the Gyron Junior survived to be installed eventually in the Blackburn Buccaneer strike aircraft and the experimental Bristol 188 machines.

Exciting developments in gas turbine technology are still to come, particularly following recent researches into materials such as titanium and fuels based on hydrogen. The wildest dreams of the jet engine pioneers are becoming reality. In the realms of supersonic flight engine systems incorporating finely matched variable geometry air intakes and jet pipe nozzles have been developed, the whole being computer controlled in conjunction with throttle movements. Technical requirements of this nature do not materialize in search of perfection for its own sake but rather to ensure the efficiency and safety which alone can yield even the smallest commercial return. A new era has begun and its possibilities present an unending challenge.

9

CONCORDE AND A BREAK
WITH TRADITION

By the mid 1950s British aircraft designers had started work on bombers that were to be not only supersonic but also capable of twice the speed of sound. The long-term prospects for the British aircraft industry appeared to be good.

But, in the end, these bombers were never built and were the first victims of the British Government's 1957 Defence White Paper which favoured the unmanned missile, both for attack and for defence. It was soon realized, however, that in certain roles, e.g. reconnaissance, manned aircraft could vary their mode of operation in a way that missiles would not be able to match for many years, if ever, and out of this thinking came the TSR.2, but even this was cancelled.

The outlook for British civil aircraft was no better than for the military. Large American jet airliners were preparing to dominate the commercial markets, and having burdened themselves with far too many separate projects, British aircraft manufacturers were in no position to compete. Some load shedding was thus inevitable and the Government also saw the need to create larger and more internationally competitive industrial units by forcing amalgamation on the aircraft constructors. This involved the disappearance of many famous company names and by 1964 two large groups had emerged for the construction of fixed wing aircraft: the British Aircraft Corporation and Hawker-Siddeley Aviation Limited. Of the major firms Handley-Page alone stayed out of the grouping and paid the penalty in 1970 when they had to cease trading. A rotating wing group was also formed but is of no direct concern to this book.

Apart from Short Bros who were already partly Government owned, Fairey's and Boulton Paul who had both already ceased to be major airframe manufacturers, the make-up of the new groups from the original firms was as follows:

British Aircraft Corporation Limited
Bristol Aircraft Limited
English Electric Aviation Limited
Hunting Aircraft Limited
Vickers-Armstrongs (Aircraft) Limited

Hawker-Siddeley Aviation Limited
Blackburn Aircraft Company Limited
Folland Aircraft Limited
Hawker Aircraft Limited
de Havilland Aircraft Company Limited
A. V. Roe and Company Limited
Whitworth-Gloster Aircraft Limited

On the engine side, two main groupings were also formed, Rolls-Royce and Bristol-Siddeley Engines, before being merged under the name of Rolls-Royce.

The obvious advantages of this upheaval met with considerable opposition, mostly of a sentimental origin. A similar situation had, however, once faced the shipping industry. After the slump of the 1930s, arrangements had to be made for a resumption of work on the giant ocean liner *Queen Mary* (then unnamed and known by the famous number 534). Public money clearly had to be injected to save the project, and sanction for this was given on condition that the two major shipping lines of Cunard and White Star would enter into a merger, or joint working agreement. The Cunard–White Star Line thus came into being, the names of both companies being retained for many years, and combined, they presented to foreign competitors a strength which neither alone possessed.

It was out of the confused background of the 1956–7 period that a practical British interest in supersonic transport aircraft arose. No dramatic moment marked the early days, but when proposals for supersonic bombers were being reviewed, both by Ministry and industry personnel, the possibility of substituting passengers for bombs was frequently discussed. The idea gained impetus when the future of military designs was promising and a continuation of supersonic research seemed assured.

A letter was thus written from the RAE to the Secretary of the Ministry of Supply suggesting that a supersonic transport aircraft might be feasible and should be actively investigated. In typically British fashion a committee was subsequently formed to explore the subject. Known as the

Supersonic Transport Aircraft Committee (STAC), it first met on 5 November 1956, and in view of the political wrangling which ultimately surrounded its protégé, it was perhaps appropriate that this meeting should be held on the 351st anniversary of the Gunpowder Plot.

The terms of reference were 'To initiate and monitor a co-operative programme of aimed research designed to pave the way for a possible first generation of supersonic transport aircraft'. Meetings were held every few months until 9 March 1959, when STAC reported its conclusions to the Controller of Aircraft in the new Ministry of Aviation. The idea had previously seemed rather remote, but as a result of the STAC exercise a clear technical policy emerged to bring safe supersonic travel within reach of the general public. But the financing of such an undertaking was likely to be beyond the resources of any one European country. A partner was therefore sought and in November 1962, just six years after the first meeting of STAC, the British Minister of Aviation, Mr Julian Amery, and the French Ambassador to Great Britain, M. Geoffrey de Courcel, signed an agreement on behalf of their respective countries to construct, jointly, a supersonic passenger transport aircraft; all work and costs to be shared equally between them.

When STAC first met, the sound barrier had lost some of its novelty and mystery, but although experimental and fighter-type aircraft exceeded the speed of sound almost daily it was only for short periods during any one flight, so the thrust to overcome supersonic drag and the high fuel consumption that went with it were likewise needed for only short periods. For this reason a small increase in supersonic drag over the design value was not necessarily serious as it increased only marginally the total fuel required for a whole flight.

Similarly with kinetic heating; the highest temperatures were sustained perhaps for only a few minutes and then only on the outer skin, so there was no time for heat to build up and soak into the structure and equipment.

A supersonic transport, however, had to go faster than sound for most of its flight. Therefore extreme efforts were needed to reduce drag, otherwise the fuel consumption would be uneconomic in the sense that fuel would have to take the place of passengers and fuel did not pay a fare.

If prolonged kinetic heating was present the problems were equally severe, as considerable quantities of heat then had time to find a way into the whole structure and into some of the equipment. At twice the speed of sound the temperature rise was no less than 170°C, so, even in a surrounding air temperature of minus 60°C, such as exists at high altitude, the skin temperature in places could exceed 110°C, which is above the boiling point of water. By comparison, on an aircraft cruising in the same air at just below the speed of sound, say, at 600 miles/h, the temperature rise was only 40°C, causing the skin temperature to increase from minus 60°C to minus 20°C at the most, and this was not only below boiling point but still well below freezing.

The two critical problems of a supersonic transport were therefore how to reduce cruising drag and how to cope with kinetic heating. Let us take these in this order and see to what extent Concorde offered a solution.

As we mentioned briefly in Chapter 1, a supersonic aeroplane had to be slender in the sense that the wing span had to be much less than the length. This was to keep the wings completely behind the nose shock wave, a layout which reduced shock wave drag. One solution was to have a straight, very thin, stub wing (e.g. the Lockheed F104), but this would have too small an area to carry the loads of a transport aircraft and would be too thin to contain fuel. Fuel tanks could of course be put in the fuselage but again this would be in place of passengers.

For these reasons the slender delta wing, now seen on Concorde, came into the reckoning, as it combined the low wave drag of a small span with a large lifting area. The wing volume was also sufficient to carry the fuel. A supersonic transport therefore began to seem possible but so far the talk had been only of high speeds. When landing speeds were considered the situation at first looked far from hopeful.

If a wing is to maintain lift as speed decreases then the angle between the wing and the airflow must be increased. (This can be checked by holding a piece of flat cardboard or even a hand out of a motor-car window at various speeds. If the cardboard is not very stiff, one can also observe flutter !) If the angle is increased beyond a certain point the airflow can no longer follow the wing contour and it breaks away (or separates) over the leading edge. At this stage, according to traditional aerodynamics, the lift is either partly or totally destroyed and the wing is said to stall.

Until speeds approached that of sound a stall had been the result either of flying too slowly or of performing severe manoeuvres, and the flow separated across most of the wing span. In all other conditions of flight large-scale separation was not expected but there was always separation at the wing tips in the form of rapidly rotating vortices (like stretched out whirlpools) streaming backwards from each tip. These vortices caused drag but with the large wing spans used on traditional aircraft they covered only a very small area of wing, so their drag was only a small part of the total.

Transonic flight unfortunately changed this simple situation and separation was sometimes experienced even in level cruising flight. This could be due to shock waves, to the sweep back of the wing, or to both, and could give rise to buffeting or unpleasant trim changes. Either way separation was still looked upon as undesirable.

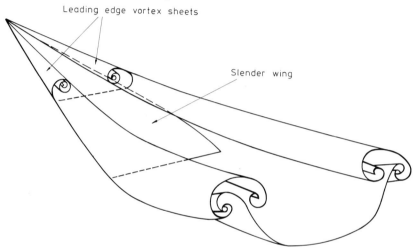

Figure 19. Airflow over a slender wing showing separated flow in form of large vortices.

But when a wing sweepback of over 50 degrees was proposed, particularly with a delta wing, it was realized that permanent flow separation might be difficult to prevent over large areas of wing surface. Did this therefore mean that the slender delta was useless as a lifting device at low speed and was the idea of a supersonic passenger transport too difficult after all?

The slender delta was of course little more than two wing tips stuck together so, in the manner of all wing tips, the airflow separated into permanent vortices. But the scale of these vortices was what mattered. They were massive (see Fig. 19), and although, not surprisingly, they

235

produced large drag, their rapid rotation over what was now not just an enlarged wing tip but actually a wing surface, also gave a surprising degree of extra lift, sufficient in fact to bring the landing speed of a supersonic transport within manageable bounds.

This then called for a complete reversal of philosophy. Just as traditional aerodynamics had required the airflow to be permanently attached for all phases of flight the same now had to be true of separation. What really mattered, in either case, was that the flow should be controllable and should not change suddenly from one type to the other. If it did the familiar trim changes and buffeting might be extreme to say the least.

There was thus a need to understand fully the physical nature of separated flow and an early and valuable contribution to this was made in 1955 by E. C. Maskell, of the Aerodynamics Department of RAE Farnborough, in a report entitled 'Flow Separation in Three Dimensions'. This report set out a more precise theory of separation than was available from earlier and more crude descriptions and was one of the first links in the Concorde chain of research. At the same time the Head of RAE Aerodynamics Department at the time, Dr Dietrich Küchemann, was directing a considerable effort towards the separation problem, to which he personally made a large contribution.

By the end of 1955 the study of separated flow had reached a stage at which it was worth examining the results of research by various organizations, and in December of that year, at a design conference held at the RAE Bedford, one session was devoted to separated flow. The discussion was opened by Mr G. H. Lee, then Assistant Chief Designer of Handley-Page Aircraft Limited, who said:

> There has been a remarkable growth of knowledge on this subject in the last two years. The aircraft firms are very interested in the gain in lift associated with the leading edge separation. The slim delta wing has many good qualities and there is some promise that an aeroplane can be designed with similar flow throughout the whole speed range.

Handley-Page had been working towards a 'flying-wing' type airliner for some time, and although by no means alone in investigating separated flow they were among the first to direct this work towards a specific transport aircraft, thereby anticipating to some extent the later work of the STAC. Photograph 53, taken in a Handley-Page wind-tunnel, demonstrates vortex formation over a delta wing. It is probably the earliest to show the effect so clearly.

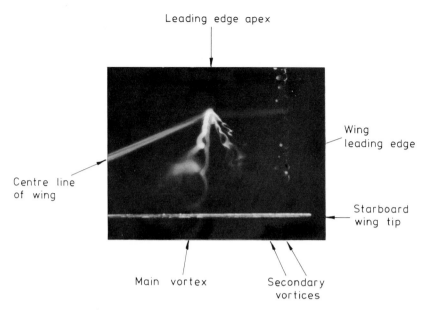

Leading edge apex

Wing leading edge

Centre line of wing

Starboard wing tip

Main vortex

Secondary vortices

Photograph 53. Photograph taken in Handley-Page wind-tunnel showing separated flow in the form of a vortex system over a slender delta wing.
(Mr Godfrey Lee)

When the Supersonic Transport Aircraft Committee first met there was thus already a sound basis for progress. Even so, legend had it that British aviation was still suffering an almost irretrievable loss of supersonic know-how caused primarily by the Miles M52 episode. The fact that both the Fairey Delta 2 and English Electric P1 were by then well on the way to twice the speed of sound, and that the Delta 2 had recently broken the world speed record, received little emphasis. In terms of numbers Britain certainly still had few supersonic aircraft, but the few had been outstanding.

Within the terms of reference of the STAC, opportunities were given for members to discuss all aspects of a job before major decisions became necessary. (In much the same way that the earlier Gas Turbine Collaboration Committee had promoted jet engines.) To this end it was composed of a main committee, a sub-committee, and various group leaders in specialized subjects. At the time of the STAC report the following Government and industrial organizations were members:

A. V. Roe & Company
Sir W. G. Armstrong-Whitworth Aircraft
Bristol Aircraft
English Electric Company
Fairey Aviation Company
de Havilland Aircraft Company
Handley-Page
Short Brothers and Harland
Vickers-Armstrongs
Armstrong-Siddeley Motors
Bristol Aero Engines
de Havilland Engine Company
Rolls-Royce
British European Airways
British Overseas Airways Corporation
Ministry of Transport and Civil Aviation
Ministry of Supply

The biggest initial problems were simply how supersonic should the new airliner be and what main route should it serve? Three possibilities emerged, these being: to fly

(1) The London–New York route with 100 to 150 passengers at about twice the speed of sound (M=2); or

(2) Short routes with 100 passengers at 1·2 times the speed of sound (M=1·2); or

(3) The London–New York and longer routes at three times the speed of sound (M=3).

For the third of these proposals (M=3) the kinetic heating would have been much more severe even than on Concorde, so the well-tried aluminium alloy could not be used for the skin. As with the earlier problem of high temperatures on jet-propulsion engines, there were therefore two possibilities. First, to use existing materials and somehow to provide cooling. Second, to use other materials which could stand the heat. It was

238

obviously out of the question to cool a large structure for long periods, so alternative materials were the only answer, and this meant using both stainless steel and titanium. However, the manufacturing costs of these would, at the time, have been prohibitive, so clearly the immediate practical limit for a supersonic transport was about twice the speed of sound.

There were, nevertheless, a few who pressed for a bold approach to $M=3$. Some even thought of adding to the problems by using a wing with variable sweepback; in other words swept fully back for high speed but almost in the classical straight position at the lowest speeds, say, for landing.

In this way the drag produced by flow separation on a swept wing would be avoided and would give lower thrust, lower fuel consumption, lower landing speed, and improved low-speed handling, all these being desirable in a passenger aircraft.

This of course was the theory, but the need to pivot the wings did pose unknown mechanical engineering problems. Experiments with variable sweep had in fact been started in Britain as early as 1949 by Dr Barnes Wallis (later Sir Barnes), of Vickers-Armstrongs (Aircraft) Limited, using a flying model known as Wild Goose (Photograph 54). This featured a separate fuselage, but on a later model, the Swallow, the fuselage was replaced by a central fixed wing of slender delta form.

Wallis had been studying variable sweep since 1945, his main aim being a laminar flow tailless passenger aircraft capable of very long range at very great heights. Non-stop flight from Europe to Australia was a primary objective. Naturally this work involved expense both by Vickers and by the Government but, unlike Wallis, the Government were more interested in military possibilities. Wallis therefore also had to pursue military applications as a source of funds to promote his general ideas but, in the end, the all-embracing White Paper of 1957 called a halt even to this work.

An approach was therefore made to the American Mutual Weapons Development Programme office in Paris, one result being the visit in 1958 to America of a team led by Wallis. This was followed by an agreement between Britain and America to conduct a short programme of joint research and the Americans were shown the British results. This was hardly surprising as they were being asked for financial aid, but some critics, even to this day, allege that British variable sweep (or more

Photograph 54. 'Wild Goose'. An experimental model aircraft with wings of variable sweepback. This was the first of a series tested by Sir Barnes Wallis, and is shown here mounted on a launching trolley.
(British Aerospace)

popularly swing-wing) technology was, in the process, handed to the Americans on a plate.

In fact the Americans were thinking of quite different applications of variable sweep to those of Wallis, and from their own wind-tunnel tests they were not in any case entirely convinced of the British claims. Their interest was in a fairly conventional military aircraft with the usual tailplane layout to operate under flight conditions very different from those of a long-range transport. The Americans had, moreover, in 1951 already flown a subsonic manned research aircraft with variable sweep, the Bell X5, based on a German design, so were not totally ignorant of the matter, although British work on wing pivot location had much to offer.

However, in a report written by the Ministry of Supply in 1959, it was admitted that variable sweep, as proposed by Barnes Wallis, might have large advantages for extreme distances. For other forms of flight it was hinted that more attractive ideas were emerging, one of which, of course, was separated flow. Variable sweep was not therefore in itself a sort of aerodynamic 'El Dorado'.

The general research into variable sweep was nevertheless continued at Vickers-Armstrongs but this time for military use. Eventually, when it seemed likely that a fighter aircraft with variable sweep would be built, a full-scale wing sweep mechanism was built at Weybridge by what had, by then, become the British Aircraft Corporation. With this device the mechanical engineering problems of the wing pivot were resolved, to the later advantage of aircraft such as the Tornado.

To go back to the STAC alternatives, the lower speed M=1·2 design was at first thought to be a reasonable step to take but this eventually seemed to need as much aerodynamic development as for M=2, so, as the latter figure gave a more worthwhile reduction of flying time, it became the target at least for aerodynamic reasons.

So the main stream of British supersonic transport research was directed to achieving a transatlantic crossing at about twice the speed of sound, and once the STAC report had assessed the various possibilities, feasibility studies could begin. These divided into two major streams, one to investigate pure flying wing layouts and the other to consider a tailless type with the more conventional fuselage for crew and passengers. Hawker-Siddeley undertook the first variant and the Bristol Aeroplane Company concentrated on the second. A flying wing would of course have had to be fairly thick to accommodate passengers. With a conventional fuselage the wing could be very thin and this layout finally proved to have decisive advantages not only for reducing drag but also in coping with balance, trim, and stability changes. Another advantage of a separate fuselage was in planning for possible increases in aircraft size and something of this was mentioned in Chapter 3.

Eventually a report on the feasibility studies was written by the staff of the RAE Farnborough and other Ministry units. It was issued on 9 May 1960, and among its recommendations two in particular are noteworthy.

Concerning variable geometry and vertical take-off

That work on these topics in the course of the feasibility studies, although not extensive, had done nothing to alter the view that they were unsuitable for a first generation of supersonic transport.

241

Concerning the M=2 airliner concept

That in spite of certain difficulties a basically aluminium supersonic transport for flight at around M=2 was feasible and that such an aeroplane would have the possibility of considerable development. If Great Britain was to stay in aviation it was recommended that a design contract for such an aeroplane be placed.

The Bristol Aeroplane Company was therefore instructed to proceed with designs for a supersonic transport aircraft having the separate fuselage and wing layout, and in August 1961 two designs were submitted, the first for M=2 and the second for M=3, despite the known difficulties of the latter. A condition of this contract was that the chances of sharing the workload with, perhaps, France, Germany, or America should be investigated.

Germany was not interested, and America, with typical big thinking, had set her sights on M=3. This left France, who had fortunately advanced some way towards a supersonic airliner of her own. French thinking originally favoured a short-range aircraft, leaving the trans-atlantic route open to American monopoly, but Britain finally insisted that only by aiming for the American route could the cost of the project be recouped. Such differences of opinion were to be expected in the initial negotiations but both countries had similar basic ideas, and when joint appraisal commenced a compromise was not too difficult.

Meanwhile, in Britain, many individual research activities were being co-ordinated in support of the STAC recommendations. More and more wind-tunnel models were used to investigate both low- and high-speed problems. In addition, rocket-powered models roared across special ranges and yet other types were quietly dropped from helicopters. Advanced electronic control and recording systems were incorporated in these models which would have been greatly welcomed ten years previously. Something of the earlier tests was discussed in Chapter 3.

The research growth between 1956 and the final signing of the Concorde agreement was such that by November 1962 about 350 models had been tested in relation to slender wing work alone and even then a final shape had not been decided. The almost complete lack of wind-tunnel or model testing in support of some early swept wing designs was in direct contrast and highlights the origin of some of their troubles.

Despite all this model and theoretical work on the supersonic airliner, however, it was never intended to dispense with manned aircraft testing, as the effectiveness of aircraft flying controls in the presence of separated flow was somewhat in doubt. The final outcome of the STAC can in fact be said to consist mainly of two research aircraft, with which we shall deal now.

Of paramount importance was the need to obtain flying experience with slender delta wings, particularly at the slow speeds necessary for landing. There was considerable impatience to do this. Some internal RAE correspondence of the time mentions 'the possibility of building, quickly, a "Santos-Dumont" type aeroplane with a maximum speed of only 250 miles/h.' (Santos-Dumont, an aviation pioneer, had built a typical aeroplane of his day and one of the most ungainly.) Although it was not intended to conduct slender wing research on quite such a primitive structure, the analogy emphasized that significant information could be gained without great expense.

The idea was accepted and resulted in one of the most useful and cheap research aircraft ever built anywhere. A specification for the type was issued early in 1959 and from a few proposals a Handley-Page design, the HP.115, was selected (Photograph 55). This possessed simple unpowered controls and a Viper jet engine for thrust. So, after all, Handley-Page played an important part in promoting a supersonic airliner. Mr G. H. Lee, whose words we previously quoted, recorded some memories of this aircraft for the purpose of this book:

> The wing leading edge of the HP.115 had 76° of sweep and was straight for the first two-thirds of its length and then curved round smoothly to produce a plan form having stream-wise tips. This plan form was chosen because it was sufficiently extreme to ensure the development of fully separated vortex flow for most flight regimes and had the merit of being the same plan form that had been the subject of numerous theoretical calculations and wind tunnel tests. The aeroplane was therefore directly comparable (in so far as the wing was concerned) with early theoretical and experimental evidence.
>
> At Handley Page we felt proud of the HP.115 because it was in fact a world First since it was the first time in the history of aviation that a man-carrying aeroplane had operated with the separated leading edge vortex flow.
>
> In practice, the general handling proved to be a great deal easier than had been expected and RAE have been able to operate the aeroplane down to speeds a lot lower than we had ever dared to hope in the early days. Handling in cross winds was much less troublesome than expected. General flying was easy and the aircraft could easily be flown by normal pilots.

Photograph 55. The Handley-Page 115. An experimental low-speed slender delta aircraft built to support the Concorde programme. The first aircraft to fly with permanently separated airflow.
(British Aerospace)

Mr Lee's comments on the handling are backed up by pilots who flew the HP.115. Theoretical studies and tests using a simulator had indicated that control of the aircraft might be unpleasant but would be acceptable if flying was limited to only the best weather. In the end the HP.115 proved delightful to fly and Squadron Leader (later Wing Commander) J. M. Henderson, who made the first flight on 17 August 1961, said in a lecture to the Royal Aeronautical Society in January 1963:

> . . . I landed bubbling over with enthusiasm over the aircraft's experimental potential. In one sense, Mr Lee of Handley Page Limited, was right when he said that the aircraft had done its main job that day by proving that the shape flew successfully.
>
> . . . The sharp leading edges seem to have had their intended effect and there has been no evidence of the vortices wandering and causing unpleasant variations in the lateral control forces and directional trim as has happened with some other aircraft. . . .

So that was it. The shape could fly and most important of all could fly safely at the low speeds needed for landing. Some amazing demonstrations were subsequently given of a low-speed rolling oscillation possible with such an aircraft. In this, the machine rocked from side to side (about 60 degrees either way) and appeared to be completely out of control. In fact the motion could be stopped quickly and at will.

It was heartening for those with faith in the slender wing to have such an early and convincing success. The next stage was to tackle higher-speed flight testing and this was where the Fairey Delta 2 came into the picture

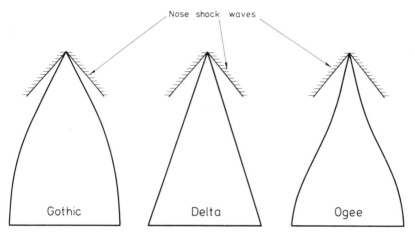

Figure 20. Variations on the slender delta wing theme. (Concorde makes use of the ogee planform.)

after its conversion by the British Aircraft Corporation into what then became known as the BAC.221.

The original 60 degree delta wing was replaced by an ogee planform as illustrated in Fig. 20. This was developed mainly at the RAE Bedford and contrasted with the plain but adequate delta shape of the HP.115 and was more representative of the full-size aircraft wing. The fuselage was lengthened by six feet and, to cope with the very high angles of incidence on landing, a longer undercarriage was fitted. Later modifications included an improved view cockpit canopy and an eight inch extension of the fin. Photograph 56a shows the 221 in flight and Photograph 56b shows Concorde and the general similarity to the much smaller 221.

245

Photograph 56a. The BAC 221. This aircraft was a converted Fairey Delta 2 and, like the Handley-Page 115, was used in support of the Concorde programme.

Photograph 56b. Concorde. The similarity between Concorde and the BAC 221 (Photograph 56a) is well shown in this view.
(British Aerospace)

This aircraft also devoted much of its time to control in the critical low-speed flying régime, where much of the design cost of a high-speed aeroplane is expended. Although fast, it was slower than the original FD.2 by virtue of its increased surface area and weight. This was not, however, of great importance. The flying controls of the BAC.221, although powered, were not, in either layout or action, the most suitable for simulating the behaviour of larger machines, but in the time available it was not worth making major changes.

Particularly necessary were tests during the approach and landing. These would show if the encouraging results obtained with the HP.115 could be reproduced on an aircraft of much higher performance. The low-speed tests were novel as a normally recognized wing stall involving flow separation could not exist with the flow already separated, and herein lay a potential danger. What had, until the coming of vortex lift, been called a conventional aircraft, possessed a distinctive habit of losing height rapidly following a stall. Warnings of the stall, either natural or built in, consisted of effects such as buffeting, rapid rolling, or nose dropping to varying degrees. With separated flow and the absence of this conventional stall the significant speed was that below which level flight could not be sustained. Hence the importance of manned flight testing to determine the minimum speed to give a margin of safety.

Sudden large speed decreases during an approach did, in fact, occur occasionally on the 221 while the pilots' attention was distracted. This emphasized the nature of the problem and the need for automatic control, particularly of the throttles.

Although the flying controls of the BAC.221 were, as we have said, not ideal for the tests in hand, this did not prevent a useful overall picture of the aircraft's handling qualities from being obtained. In a Technical Report by the RAE Bedford the following opinions of the 221 were expressed.

In spite of control system deficiencies the BAC.221 was described as pleasant to handle in all respects. One pilot some six months after he last flew the aircraft remembered it as an 'unremarkable aeroplane'. Test pilots are reasonably accustomed to remarkable or demanding research aircraft and possibly their judgement in this respect would be less severe than that of others, but nevertheless, such a comment on a radically new aircraft, after flight in it at the limiting extremes of its flight envelope can almost be regarded as a compliment.

But if the model and full-scale flight programme was sorting out the aerodynamics, the structure remained a problem, even for a speed no greater than twice that of sound. One of the main uncertainties was that Concorde was to be the largest supersonic aircraft so far built and its skin would consist of larger sheets of aluminium alloy than had previously been subjected to high temperatures. There was no reason to think that these sheets would not retain their strength in this form but would they retain their carefully designed shape? If not, a serious rise of drag might be difficult to prevent and this would destroy the already marginal operating economics.

With reasonable luck the Bristol 188 and TSR.2 might have gone some way to providing part of the answer but their premature demise of course prevented sufficiently extensive tests. What would have been learned from them? The simple answer is nobody knows. The worst effects of kinetic heating did not occur merely at the highest temperature. Each increase and decrease of temperature produced stresses which reduced the fatigue life of the structure. Innumerable combinations of conditions had to be considered and the difficulties were expressed clearly by Mr James Taylor, then of the RAE Farnborough, when delivering the fifteenth Mitchell Memorial Lecture to the Royal Aeronautical Society on 14 February 1968. Speaking in the discussion, he said:

> . . . on the thermal cycles we merely know that there is an effect on just about everything you can think of, such as if you put the temperature on first and then the load it will be different from putting on the load without temperature and then the temperature afterwards; just about everything you can do has an effect and some of these effects are likely to be quite important.

The reaction of the Concorde structure to its environment could not therefore be understood fully by building up hours just on the aircraft themselves. The risks were too great. Had an upper Mach number limit of 1·8 been accepted (and many favoured this) the time or expense of much ground testing could have been saved. But by going for 2·2, or even 2, it seemed that the extra cost might turn marginal economics into real profit. On the other hand a disaster even greater than the Comet might be the 'reward'. It was one of those decisions so often attending a major advance and the more difficult course was selected of extracting the last ounce of performance from the structure.

Mr Taylor, in his lecture, touched on this decision, and said:

> I do not mean you should not try and make it above 2·2 for aluminium alloy . . . you must take special precautions and I think I did hint . . . that 100°C was all right for long term, but for short term you might even go up to 150°C.

Therefore I agree . . . that at 2·2 you would be all right for the first few months whatever happened, but after that you are relying on the fatigue strength of the aircraft. If we could guarantee the 2·2 we would not have been contemplating the very expensive Concorde airframe test at Farnborough.

Expensive in this case included an outlay of three million pounds on one of the most comprehensive structural test facilities yet erected. In a large test building opened by Her Majesty Queen Elizabeth II on Monday, 6 June 1966, a complete Concorde airframe, with the exception of the tips of the wings and fin, is now encased in ducts from which air of varying temperature is passed over the outer skin. A supply of fuel, also capable of being heated, is fed through the fuel system to simulate in-flight conditions. These tests into the behaviour of metals at prolonged high temperatures will, in the end, benefit technologies outside aviation so at least some of the cost of Concorde may be repaid indirectly.

There is no doubt, however, that even if future supersonic transports are restricted to twice the speed of sound they will contain a smaller proportion of aluminium alloy than Concorde. This is due to great progress in the techniques of fabricating that remarkable metal titanium, the bulk of which in alloy form has so far been applied to aerospace work.

Titanium was discovered in 1790 by an English clergyman, William Gregory, during his studies of black beach sands in Cornwall. Then in 1932, Dr Wilhelm Kroll, a native of Luxembourg, devised a method of extracting metallic titanium which, in 1947, was developed into a commercial production process by the Americans. The features of titanium alloys are their strength, their light weight, and their resistance to both heat and corrosion. The alloys of some other metals separately display one or two of these properties perhaps to a greater degree than titanium but so far none has combined all four in one alloy at a level so attractive to aircraft engineers. The much used aluminium alloys have always been very prone to corrosion and, despite the rigorous inspection common to aircraft operation, undetected corrosion has been the cause of several spectacular accidents.

It is, therefore, not surprising that over a period of twenty-five years, since commercial quantities were first available in the early 1950s, titanium has become the ninth major industrial metal. Now that it can be produced and manipulated more easily the sales of titanium have grown enormously, so the price has come down and exciting new developments in aircraft design are possible.

In the meanwhile, the entry into service of Concorde has not seen the end of structural research on the type as inservice experience is daily adding to ground test experience. On this hopeful note we will therefore leave the subject of structures and end this story by describing, first, the highly advanced engine installation and then the systems which operate Concorde and sustain life aboard her.

The selection of engines for Concorde was perhaps a more certain operation than the aerodynamic and structural design of the airframe. Separated flow and kinetic heating even if understood in principle needed many hours of in-flight investigation to be sure of their effects. Engine requirements on the other hand were based on an enormous background of experience both in the air and on test beds. Most of this may have been at subsonic speeds but, as we saw in Chapter 8, the means of increasing jet engine performance and utilization were understood and capable of calculation from their earliest days.

An advanced version of the Olympus twin-spool turbo-jet engine, the Type 593, was eventually chosen for Concorde. Intended to deliver 38 000 lb of thrust with reheat it became the first reheated engine used in civil operation. What factors influenced this choice?

The first decision was whether a straight jet or some form of bypass engine would be most suitable. Ram jets or compound turbo-ram jets were more applicable to Mach numbers of above three so did not enter the deliberations. In the search for subsonic economy, experience had shown bypass engines to be desirable. At high supersonic speeds, however, their frontal area, weight, and bulk were larger than for straight jets and gave a drag high enough to cancel out a slightly better test bed fuel consumption. Thus the straight jet won the day, at least on the economy front, but some concern was, and still is, expressed from the noise aspect, and these questions are still being urgently pursued.

With the basic engine layout established, it remained to decide whether a new design would be needed or an existing type could be adapted to suit, but time quickly resolved this problem simply by allowing no time to develop a new engine.

British engines designed particularly for supersonic work had in any case had an unfortunate history. Starting with the special W2/700 system for the cancelled Miles M52 there then followed the de Havilland Gyron, which lacked a customer, although being at one time booked for the private venture Hawker 1121. Its offspring, the Gyron Junior, had a disappointing career in the Bristol 188 as far as it went, and the combined rocket/jet engine of the SR.53 never progressed to a production version. The ill-fated TSR.2 almost changed the tradition but with its particular variant of the Olympus even this aircraft had no chance to accumulate flying hours, so some valuable supersonic engine, as well as structural experience, was lost following this sensational cancellation.

Prior to Concorde, British supersonic engine work had been wholly military in emphasis and primarily concerned with the Avon powered Lightning and Fairey Delta 2 aircraft. In particular, a valuable series of engine tests was made with an FD.2, both with and without reheat, and extensive comparisons between in-flight and test bed results were obtained, this being the first time that such comprehensive and accurate data had been obtained for a reheat installation. Civil versions of the Avon were, of course, wholly subsonic. It is interesting to recall that a six Avon installation was proposed in the advanced Bomber report of 1947 and that some fifteen years later six of these same engines were, in later form, included in design studies of the supersonic transport. Of the bombers the Vulcan ended up, like the Concorde, as a delta wing aircraft with four Olympus. To show the progress made with this engine in recent years Table 9 gives a brief comparison.

Table 9

	Military Olympus 301 (as fitted to Vulcan BMk2)	Supersonic transport Olympus 593 (as fitted to Concorde)
Take-off thrust (without reheat)	20 000 lb	35 000 lb
Mass flow	290 lb/s	450 lb/s
Pressure ratio	13 : 1	15 : 1
Length (engine alone)	131 in	138 in
Diameter (inlet)	44·5 in	47·9 in
Weight	4290 lb	5600 lb
Low pressure compressor	6 stage	7 stage
High pressure compressor	7 stage	7 stage

As can be seen the thrust has increased by 75 per cent for only a 5 per cent increase in engine length and a 30 per cent increase in weight.

Why, it might be asked, were the military supersonic engines inadequate for civil use? The answer is that they were really subsonic designs capable of occasional boosting to much greater thrust by reheat, the very high fuel consumption resulting from this expedient being tolerated, as we have seen, because of its short duration. When it came to a supersonic airliner a continuously high turbine temperature was necessary for economy and this was all too easy to achieve, thanks to kinetic heating. The temperatures in the rest of the engine, however, were also raised, so much of the compressor blading had to be changed from aluminium alloy to titanium, and the final compressor stage and the remaining 'hot' parts of the engine were made mainly of new high-temperature nickel alloys. Even with these, however, the turbine blades could not withstand the heat and stress, so cooling air had to be passed through each blade. Bristol-Siddeley engines had not previously featured blade cooling but it had been fitted to some Rolls-Royce Avon engines and these had flown for many hours. As yet there is no alternative to this added bit of complexity and the magnitude of the engine temperature problem is clear when it is realized that before entering the Olympus combustion chambers the air has already reached a temperature of 600°C.

Having designed an engine to cruise at over twice the speed of sound, what about its use for take-off, climb, descent, landing, and any other operational condition? As aircraft speeds increase in the supersonic range and the conditions accumulate under which the engine is expected to be efficient, a fixed area intake and jet pipe nozzle no longer gives the best efficiency for each condition, so a variable area is needed. An analogy with human body operation can again be drawn. When sitting or walking it is sufficient to breathe in just through the nose. At a quick walking or running pace, however, particularly on a hot day or in the thin air of high ground, the lungs soon need to inhale more air than the nose can deliver. The mouth is then used to cope with this extra demand.

What would happen if only a simple fixed air intake was provided? If this delivered the right quantity of air at, say, $M=1$, then for $M=2$ the quantity would be too big and surplus air would 'spill' out, resulting in excess drag. At, say, $M=0.5$, the same intake would be too small and the engine would be starved of air. Either way uneconomic flight would result. At speeds other than the two quoted, the adequacy of the simple intake would vary depending on how near to the design datum of $M=1$ the aircraft flew. In other words, with a variable system the intake or exhaust areas would ideally change continuously in response to small attitude, temperature, and pressure changes, just as aircraft autostabilizers work continuously.

No human engineer could of course operate the system with sufficient and prolonged accuracy, so control by electronic computer is incorporated in Concorde. Its performance is being watched with the greatest interest, playing, as it does, such a vital part in the operating economics.

The Concorde engine testing programme has comprised both in-flight and ground facilities. In the absence of the TSR.2 no aircraft of cruising performance comparable to Concorde was available to conduct airborne testing in advance of the prototype's first flight. Much could, however, be done to explore the take-off, landing, and other lower-speed regions. For this there existed just the right aircraft in the Vulcan. Being a large delta its attitudes in flight and particularly for landing were similar to Concorde, so it was equipped to carry an Olympus 593 in a complete Concorde engine nacelle slung under the fuselage (see earlier Photograph 45c). What was learned from this experiment? Although the Vulcan could not exceed a Mach number of 0·98, this was enough to investigate all the subsonic side of the engine behaviour, including intake and engine anti-icing. The functioning of engine components and instruments, the response of the engine to changes of throttle movement, aircraft attitude, height, and speed, and some performance measurements were all undertaken without any risk to Concorde itself.

To extend testing beyond the Vulcan capability required extensive ground tests. A major part of this work was conducted in a complex facility known as Cell 4 at the National Gas Turbine Establishment at Pyestock. Here the engine and intake control systems were tested under conditions equivalent to Mach numbers up to 2·35 and altitudes up to 70 000 ft.

From the impressive power and noise of engines we finally turn to the unobtrusive mechanical and electrical systems lying beneath the aircraft skin (Photograph 57). These are the arteries, nerves, and muscles of Concorde, and although perhaps not having an impact on the imagination comparable to wing and engine design are just as vital. There are two basic types of system, those for operating the aircraft and those for sustaining life aboard her. In the earliest days of flying the only system required was for fuel and this consisted simply of a tank, a short length of pipe, and a tap. Fuel feed to the engine was by gravity. As most flying then took place in the lower atmosphere no protection for aviators was needed other than thick clothing. As early as 1911, however, altitude records stood at around 15 000 ft, and although healthy people could fly at such heights without oxygen this ability was made easier by the slow rates of climb of early aircraft. (It is worth remembering that Himalayan mountaineers indulge in high-altitude acclimatization during the slow climb to the upper reaches of a mountain. Men have even stood for short periods on the summit of Everest at 29 000 ft without oxygen but they could not have done so if they had climbed the mountain in the few minutes it takes an aeroplane to reach that height.)

With the increases of speed, height, and duration of more advanced aircraft came the need for fuel pumps, retractable undercarriages, flaps, and radio aids. These had to be worked by hydraulic, pneumatic, or electrical systems, and slowly the pioneer-type flying machines evolved into the reliable aircraft we know today.

Gains of height were, of course, accompanied by reductions in air temperature and pressure so that both man and equipment needed some protection from a hostile environment.

In particular some elementary forms of cabin heating became necessary as flying times lengthened and it was not long before thought had also to be given to the supply of oxygen. It was easy to equip a young military pilot with an oxygen mask and heavy clothing but the average civil airline passenger could not, of course, be expected to enthuse over such a dentist's chair-type uniform. Fortunately, the need for passenger oxygen coincided with increases in aircraft rate of climb and the attendant rapid changes of pressure. This meant that the pressure cabins which were in any case needed in order to reduce the rates of pressure change could also supply the essential oxygen.

The external pressures at the maximum heights then flown (about 25 000 ft) were not in themselves a hazard – only the rapid changes. The situation, however, was slowly becoming more dangerous.

With the advent of jet airliners flying at 40 000 ft pressure cabins really came into their own. At such heights life can be endangered by the low atmospheric pressure alone, regardless of the amount of oxygen available. For this reason emergency pressurization had to be incorporated to cope with a limited rupture of the cabin structure or, say, the loss of a window. It was, however, just possible to save lives following cabin pressure failure at 40 000 ft provided an immediate and rapid descent could be made to lower altitudes. If this was not possible death would result but still primarily from lack of oxygen rather than pressure.

Supersonic airliners are now cruising at heights of around 60 000 ft and here the situation is quite different. The air pressure is only about one-fourteenth of that at sea-level and this causes the human blood to boil; in fact one might just as well be in outer space. No amount of oxygen can then prevent death so a completely reliable cabin pressure system is essential.

There is a further danger to pressure cabin dwellers in the domain of Concorde and this arises from the ever-present kinetic heating. Air for pressurization is extracted from the engine compressors and has to be cooled before entering the cabin. Should any failure allow outside air to enter the cabin directly, its temperature of around 150°C could be detrimental to health even if the pressure was maintained. On a normally hot day in the tropics a temperature of 45°C (113°F) would be almost unbearable to most Europeans. Imagine air at three times this temperature and the problem of passengers' protection can be appreciated.

Of the Concorde systems not directly connected with sustaining life the hydraulics and electrics continue their tradition of operating the aero-dynamic, engine, and undercarriage controls, the advent of advanced radio, radar, and navigation aids making electrical power of even greater importance than before. Both hydraulic fluid and electrical components have temperature limits and the higher temperature of supersonic cruising means either using them as they stand with a suitable cooling system or accepting the temperature and developing heat-resistant materials. In slower aircraft plenty of cooling air is available just by scooping some in from outside but with kinetic heating this simple solution is not available. In order to save the weight of an internal cooling system, every effort has therefore been made over the years to use high operating temperatures and this is now possible.

The fuel system is a most interesting development, being more than just an advance on previous work in this sphere. Surprisingly its use to supply fuel to the engine is only one-third of its job; the remainder consists of carrying away surplus heat from the structure and cabin and keeping the aircraft in trim. Although the air at 60 000 ft is very cold the aircraft structure temperature, due to kinetic heating, is so high that normal radiation can carry away hardly any heat. The surplus is therefore directed into the fuel which, by leaving the aircraft continuously in large quantities

Photograph 57. Concorde complexity. Installing equipment in Concorde. It is obvious from this view why such aircraft are expensive.
(British Aerospace)

through the engine, conveniently takes with it the unwanted heat. There are problems associated with this expedient. If the fuel was to be excessively heated deposits of gum could form in the pipes and filters, causing a complete engine stoppage. Boiling might also occur but this has always been a risk with high-flying aircraft and fuel pressurization is the cure.

The third fuel system function of trimming the aircraft is one of the new ideas introduced by Concorde; in fact, without it, the whole project would probably not have been viable. With subsonic aircraft, fuel is moved from one tank to another to keep the centre of gravity fairly constant and this reduces the need for constant trimming. But when an aircraft accelerates from subsonic to supersonic speed the aerodynamic loads, as we saw earlier, change in size and position, so the control angles must then be changed to keep the aircraft in trim. With Concorde the control surfaces could then be angled so much into the airstream that drag would seriously increase, so fuel is pumped around the fuel tanks, not, in this case, to keep the centre of gravity constant but to change it deliberately. This trims the aircraft without having to use the control surfaces. It need hardly be said that reliability of the pumping system is very important both for safety and for operational efficiency, and, as with other vital systems, duplication of parts insures against overall failure.

To test the fuel system a full-scale moving rig was constructed at the then British Aircraft Corporation's Filton works. It is shown in Photograph 58 and is one more illustration of the lengths to which testing has had to go in the interests of Concorde safety.

At the time of writing both the British and French Concordes are in service and we have traversed a time span of about 260 years from the beginning to the end of this book. Most of the action has taken place in the

Photograph 58. Concorde fuel system test rig. A considerable engineering task in itself.
(British Aerospace)

257

final sixty years during which a small part of the human race has achieved a standard of living completely unimaginable even at the start of the twentieth century. In the same period the world has witnessed ever-mounting horrors.

How does supersonic flight fit into the meaning and purpose of all this? If we believe that rapid travel can promote world peace and can assist in the maintenance of human rights then projects like Concorde may, in the long run, be worth more perhaps than economics alone can indicate. The Armageddon which in recent years has so often seemed imminent may after all be avoided and technology might even be directed more willingly to the good of the world population rather than to the struggle for land-masses and dubious ideals.

APPENDIX I

NATIONAL AERONAUTICAL
ESTABLISHMENT BEDFORD

Installation	*Value* £
General services	750 000
3 ft × 3 ft Wind-tunnel	150 000
High-speed laboratory	100 000
Spinning-tunnel	150 000
Structures laboratory	100 000
Propeller spinning-rig	125 000
13 ft × 9 ft Wind-tunnel plant (2)	40 000
General purpose aeronautics laboratory	20 000
8 ft × 8 ft Wind-tunnel plant	400 000
8 ft × 8 ft Wind-tunnel structure	750 000
Altitude plant No. 1 unit	250 000
Altitude plant final	3 000 000
Workshops	250 000
Metallurgical laboratories	50 000
Canteens and welfare	50 000
16 ft × 12 ft CA tunnel plant structure	500 000
Gas turbine power station	1 250 000
Future programme	Up to 20 000 000

The values shown are of course those applying at the time. In modern terms they would be at least ten times greater.

(Taken from Presidential address by Mr P. T. Fletcher to the Institution of Mechanical Engineers, 1975.)

EPILOGUE

When this book was started the Americans were still actively engaged on studies of a supersonic transport aircraft much larger and much faster than Concorde.

But then came the world-wide increase in oil prices, and this, together with a growing desire to reduce atmospheric pollution, made the economics of supersonic travel look rather less attractive; at least for the immediate future. Not only that but the cost of all manufactured products rose alarmingly to the extent that even the most technologically advanced nations began to collaborate to share the costs of future aircraft, both supersonic and otherwise.

For this reason it no longer seems realistic to consider the aviation industry of any one country in isolation, so we finish this story of British work by looking to the future: to new shapes in the sky, to new types of fuel, to new materials, to new partners in the job of building aircraft.

As a symbol of this future, the last picture (Photograph 59) was taken at the 1978 Society of British Aerospace Constructors show at Farnborough. It shows the Directors of two associated companies, one British and the other American, talking to the author about their common product, the metal titanium, which has become of such great importance in aerospace construction. In the foreground is a model of the Space Shuttle, an American project, which, like several others, has benefited from research in many lands, and particularly from the prolonged British work on delta wings.

This then is the pattern of the future. Pride in what has been done alone and faith in what must now be shared.

Photograph 59. The future demands international collaboration. The author (extreme right) at the 1978 Society of British Aerospace Companies Show at Farnborough talks to (left to right): George Laybourne-Smith, Sales Director of the British company Titanium Metal and Alloys Limited; E. Niles Kenyon, Vice-President, Sales, and Joe Byrne, President, of the Timet Division of the Titanium Metals Corporation of America.
(Titanium Metal and Alloys Limited)

INDEX

Cox, Dr H. Roxbee, *see also* Lord Kings-Norton, 12, 214
Cranfield, 22, 59, 224
Cranwell, RAF, 14, 194, 209, 211, 213
Creep, of materials, 204
Crescent wing, 94, **95, 134**, 135, **186**
Cripps, Sir Stafford, 58, 59
Cunard Line, 232
Cunningham, John, 104–106, 120
Curvature, surface, 10, 15, 25, 26
Cycles, thermal, 248

Damper, friction, 107
Damping of oscillation, 82, 108, 150, 196
Dart engine, Rolls-Royce, 199
Dassault, 153
Datum trimming, 131, 143
Davies, Handel, 38, 78, 92
Death rays, 215
Deck, aircraft carrier, 132
Decompression, explosive, 178, 179, **180**
Defence, Minister of, 149
    Ministry of, 37
    White Paper, 58, 169, 231, 239
Defiant fighter, ejection from, 96
de Havilland, 14, 17, 73, 97–115, 169, 216, 228, 230, 232, 238
    Comet, 175, 176–181, 201
    Geoffrey, Jnr, 17, 100, 102, 103, 104, 105
    Geoffrey, Sir, 104
    Goblin engine, 100, 216, 221
    Ghost engine, 105, 177, 220, 221
    Gyron engine, 230, 250
    Gyron Junior engine, 172, 226, 230, 250
    Type 108, 18, 52, 53, 55, 57, 62, 71, 73, 82, 86, 97–115, 150, 162, 176, 187, 196
    Vampire, 14, 17, 40, 57, 97, 99, 101, 102, 104, 105, 216
Delta aircraft, 73, 74, 89, **91**, 92, **93, 94**, 150, 151–162, 228, 237, 245, 251
    slender, 234–243
    wing, 71, 74, 77, 81, 82, 88–90, 139, 140, 152, 153, 185, 188, 235, 245, 251, 253
Demands, control, 198
Density, of fluid, 6, 26
Derry, John, 17, 18, 92, 97–115, 120, 138, 139
Derwent engine, Rolls-Royce, **21**, 78, 89, 163, 221
Dickinson, R. P., 168
Diesel engine, 206
Distortion, of structure, 12

Disturbances, 6, 70, 189
Dive, 29, 39, **49**
Dive, supersonic, 50, 97–115
Diving, 30
Douglas, Dr, 98
Douglas, Skyray (American fighter), 130
Downwash, 153
Dowty Group, 148
Drag (resistance of air), 3, 4, 12, 15, 23–26, 29, 33–39, 41, 47, 48, 51, 69, 71, 72, 74, 89, 152, 157, 165, 187, 211, 233–239, 241, 248, 257
Dresden, bombing raid on, 56
Drooped leading edge, wing, 165
Drooped nose, 156
Ducts, 20
Ducted fan, 225, 228, 229
Duke, Neville, 120, 138, 139
Dunsfold Aerodrome, 126, 137
Duplicated controls, 76, 156

Eagle, HMS, 133
Eastern Germany, 56
Effectiveness, control, 69, 86
Efficiency:
    compressor, 204
    flying, 189
    human, 189
    structural, 153
    turbine, 204
Egypt, 5
Ejector seats, 52, 80, 81, 92, 96, 105, 143, 145
Elba, Island of, 178, 179
Electrical research, 183
Electronic computer, 253
Electronics, 195, 212
Elevator, 31, 34, **36**, 74, 100, 123, 125, 135
Elevator trim tab, 31
    booster, 135
Elevon, 100, 112
Elliot, Lt 'Jock', RN, 91, 92
Emergency control (manual), 76
Emergency pressurization, 254
Emergency procedures, 175
Empire flying boats, 177
    Test Pilots School, 22, **23**, 138
Endurance, of supersonic fighters, 167
Engine anti-icing, 253
    designers, 45
    Experimental Dept, RAE, 215
    jet propulsion, 202 ff

power, 45
research, 183
sub-committee, 206, 215, 216
supersonic, 252
Engineering, mechanical, 198
Engineers, structural, 27
test, 45
English Electric, 19, 99, 140, 150, 152, 153, 163, 229, 232, 237, 238
English Electric P1 Lightning fighter, 19, 150, 151, 152, 153 ff, 229, 237
Environment, 6
Environmental testing, 116, 146, 147, 194
Equipment, effect of environment, 146
Error, altimeter, 36, **159**, 160
compressibility, 35, 37
position, 37
Esler, S. E., 89
Establishment, National Aeronautical (NAE), 59, 60, 259
National Gas Turbine (NGTE), 60, 215, 221, 228, 253
Research, 58
Royal Aircraft (RAE), 13, 14, 22, 26, 27, 28, 31, 32, 37, 38, 42, 44, 48, 50, 65, 69, 75, 76, 84, 86, 91, 98, 107, 114, 149, 150, 153, 155, 163, 191, 195, 203, 205, 206, 209, 212, 216, 220, 221, 224, 225, 226, 228, 232, 236, 243, 248
Estimates, air, 183, 184
Defence, 149
Europe, 200, 239
European routes, 18
Everest, Mount, 254
Expendable fighter, 141
Exhaust driven supercharger, 208
Experimental aircraft, 70, 74, 116
Vampire, 99
Experiments, aerodynamics, 4
Extended wing tips, 131
External contour, 157
External control surfaces, 74

Factor(s), safety, 175
Failure, fatigue, 176, 178
flying control, 178, 197 ff
pressure cabin, 179, **180**, 254
structural, 178, 181
Fairey Aviation, 19, 53, 67, 89, 93, 150 ff, 193, 231, 238
Fairey Aviation FD1, 89, 93, **94**, 155

FD2, 19, 53, 69, 89, 94, 150, **151** ff, 228, 237, 245, **246**, 247, 251
long range monoplane, **193**
Fairing, bullet, 136
Falcon, Miles 'Gilette', **54**
Fan, augmenter, 225
ducted, 225, 228, 229
Farnborough, *see* Establishment, Royal Aircraft
Fatigue, 176, 178, 179, 248, 249
Fedden, Sir Roy, 55, 59, 148, 220
Report, of visit to USA, 55, 177
Felixstowe, 211
Fences, wing, 128
Fighter aircraft, 19, 56, 57
Command RAF, 19, 28, 135
expendable, 141
experimental, 74
lightweight, 140 ff
reconnaissance, 19, 131
rocket, 46, **169**, 170
Filton, 161, 257
Finely balanced controls, 75
Finnish Air Force, 144
Firth–Brown Research Laboratories, 205
Fixed wing, proposal by Sir G. Gayley, 5
Flap(s), 25, 89, 101, 152, 156, 162, 165, 254
Flaps, blowing, 133, 172
trim, 108, 112, 113
Fletcher, P. T., 60, 259
Flexibility, control, 145, 146
Flapping wing, 5
Flight, automatic, 175, 188 ff
bird, 5
control system, 196, 201
human, 2
over weather, 209
path, 71
planning, 160
refuelling 177
research, 13, 73, 154, 161
subsonic, 24, 70 ff
supersonic, *see* Supersonic flight
testing, 22, 27, 28, 30, 32, 36, 37, 42, 45, 52, 84, 120, 121, 131, 147, 157, 160, 162, 166, 167, 173, 174, 192, 247
transatlantic, 10
transonic, 12, 15, 29, 33, 34, 37, 55 ff, 62, 70, 71, 77, 89, 116, 117
Flight, weekly magazine, 102
Flow, air, 7, 12, 29
breakaway, 80, 129

265

Gyron, *see* de Havilland
Gyroscope(s), 189, 190, 191

Halford, Major Frank, 216, 230
Hall, Sir Arnold, 179
Hampshire, 120, 140
Handley Page Aircraft Limited, 73, 96, 184,
   191, 231, 236, **237, 238**, 243, 244
Handley Page Halifax bomber, 57
   Type 88, 94, **95**, 96, 135, 146
   Type 115, 243, **244**, 245, 246, 247
   Victor bomber, 20, 94, 95, 184, 185, **186**,
      188, 228, 229
Handling, aircraft, 53, 62, 72, 80, 86, 90,
   201, 243
Hanson, Jack, 60, **61**
Hartley Wintney, 114
Hatfield, Hertfordshire, 100, 104–106
Hatfield, Dr W. H., 205
Hawker Aircraft Limited, 32, 74, 84, 126,
   130, 135, 138, 232
Hawker Hunter, 19, 88, 117, **118**, 122, 124,
   126, 130, 135, 136, **137, 138**, 139, 140,
   143, 144, 146, 148, 152, 200, 229
   Hurricane, 84
   P1040, 84
   Type 1052, 82, **83**, 84, **85**, 86
   Type 1081, 84, **85**
   Type 1121, 250
Hawker-Siddeley Aviation Limited, 144,
   231, 241
Hawker-Siddeley, Harrier, 229
   Hawk, 144
   P1127, 229
Haynes, Colonel, USAF, 158
Heat, unwanted, 256
Heating, cabin, 254
   kinetic, 172, 234, 238, 248, 250, 252, 255
Heat resistant materials, aircraft, 255, 256
   engines, 204, 205
Heavy Research Plant, Ministry of Works:
   programme, 259
   Section, 60
Height (*see also* High altitude):
   'barrier', 181
   separation, 160
   survival at, 175 ff
   true, 159
Henderson, Mr Arthur, 183
Henderson, Wing Commander, J. M., 244
High altitude dives, 29 ff

flying, 175 ff, 209
   photography, 29
High lift device(s), 25, 41, 71
High speed designs, 76
   dives, **34**, 37
   flight trials, 37
   research, 76
   tests, 13
Hilton, Dr W. F., 24
Himalayan mountaineers, acclimatization,
   254
Hindustan Aircraft Limited, 144
Historical Group, Royal Aeronautical
   Society, 48
Houston, Lady, 11
Hughes, S. R., 38
Hunting Aircraft Limited, 232
Hursley Park, 84, 123
Hydraulic systems, 146, 254, 255
Hydrogen bombs, 117
Hypersonic aircraft, 155

Ice-box, for dry air, 66
Illustrious, HMS, 87
Incidence, angle of, 89, 165
   variable, 84, 125, 129
Independently rotating compressor, 224
Indian Air Force, 144
Indicator, air speed, 36, 107, 127
Industrial Revolution, 2, 212
Instability, 82, 194
Instability pitching, 108
Installations, engine, 172, 178
Instinctive reaction, 167
Institution of Mechanical Engineers, 147,
   208
Instrumentation, 99, 109, 114, 126, 167, 197
Instrument(s), 33, 34, 38
Instruments:
   camera, 109
   cockpit, 122
   correction, 109
   research, 183, 188
   test, 109
Intake, air, 17, 20, 130
   anti-icing, 253
   fixed area, 252
   variable area, 252
Integrated defence system, 141
Intercepter fighter, 141, 169
Internal combustion turbine, 215, 216
International Congress, Zürich, 155

267

270